my escape
from the CIA
(and into CBS)

my escape
from the CIA
(and into CBS)

HUGHES RUDD

E. P. DUTTON & CO., INC., NEW YORK, 1976

GRATEFUL ACKNOWLEDGMENT IS MADE FOR PERMISSION TO RE-
PRINT THE FOLLOWING STORIES:

J. B. Lippincott Company: "The Shores of Schizophrenia" ©
1961 by Hughes Rudd • *The Paris Review:* "Miss Euayla Is the
Sweetest *Thang*" © 1961 by Hughes Rudd; "The Fishers: 1932"
© 1957 by Hughes Rudd; "The Bankrupt" © 1957 by Hughes
Rudd; "The Lower Room" © 1961 by Hughes Rudd • *Esquire:*
"Mavis at the Beach" © 1961 by Hughes Rudd • *Harper's Maga-
zine:* "My Escape from the CIA" © 1961 by Hughes Rudd; "The
Man on the Trestle" © 1952 by Hughes Rudd • *Saturday Eve-
ning Post:* "The Death of William Faulkner" © 1963 by Hughes
Rudd.

CONTENTS

foreword

❧ When this book was first published, I was based in Moscow, trying without success to report on what was going on in the Kremlin (*nobody* knows what's going on in the Kremlin, except that they always have a supply of Hungarian salami in the Kremlin kitchen, a benefit not always enjoyed by the rest of the Muscovites: my source for that is as hard as the salami itself, but I can't reveal it), and *successfully* reporting on such matters as why the Soviet Union was so upset about the Sour Pickle Shortage. For three days running *Pravda* devoted a half-page to this subject, and since the paper usually has no more than four or six pages, the Sour Pickle Shortage was obviously of state concern. "Heads will roll in the Preserved Vegetable Trust!" *Pravda* thundered at one point. It turned out that when Russian men travel on the train they take along a bottle of vodka and a sack of sour pickles to chase the vodka: the Preserved Vegetable Trust had dropped the ball, the distribution of pickles had stalled, and thousands of Soviet workers who had been ordered to leave work in Minsk for work in Oomsk were refusing to go. The Road to Communism is full of little potholes such as that.

Anyway, when the book came out, the publisher sent fifty copies of it to me, and the Moscow customs agents, undone by the title, allowed me to have only thirty-eight of them: they had no ready explanation for what happened to the other twelve, but it wasn't hard to figure out: a few weeks later a fellow I dealt with in the bureaucracy who was (is?) a Colonel in the KGB said to me during a lull in our hard-driving negotiations over whether or not CBS would be permitted to film matzoh-making at the Central Synagogue (we were doing the obligatory Passover Story), "Say, have you got another copy of your book? I *had* one, but it was stolen out of my desk here in the office." I sent him another copy, but they never *did* allow us to shoot the matzoh-making.

Some of the stories in this book are supposed to be fiction, others fact: I find it hard to tell the difference, although they are all, with one possible exception, *based* on fact. Life *is,* after all, like a tour through a lunatic asylum or a funeral parlor in Waco, Texas, or mine has been, anyway, and the thing to do is just keep moving and don't worry about a thing, as the infantry used to say. That rule, plus the love and support of the most wonderful woman in the world (who, as everybody knows, is Anna Greenwood Rudd), has made this book possible. She is sane: I often feel the rest of us are not.

New York City, October, 1975.

my escape
from the CIA
(and into CBS)

the shores
of schizophrenia

⁂ I started spouting off the other night about how I'd always wanted to have a conducted tour through a mortuary, with somebody along to explain what it was all about, exactly how they do it and so forth, when I remembered that I did take a tour like that once, although it didn't turn out too well. I'd forgotten all about it, it just shows you how useless everything is, how absurd it is to try and tell kids anything. You give them an experience like that, something you'd think they could never forget, and within a week they don't know what you're talking about.

I had to shut up when I thought of it, I was sitting in the garden behind the Peanut at one of the tin tables, swilling beer and working up to a good speech, really getting ready to insult somebody, but it plugged me right up. The other people at the table decided I hated them, they couldn't understand it, it wasn't like me at all. I just sat there, I couldn't tell them about it because they wouldn't have understood it, it would have meant a lot of babbling and shouting, before it was all over we'd have been down on the gravel, rolling around and beating each other with beer bottles while the fat rats skipped back and forth, trying to stay out of range. That's the way it is out at the Peanut, sometimes, the

9

place attracts that sort. You can curse and shout and belch all you want, as long as you don't pull anything funny, anything unusual. If you do—blooey! out you go.

That mortuary trip was just one of several we had at that time. We were in the fourth grade, somewhere around there, at Dean Highland school in Waco, Texas, a building stuck out on the muddy edge of town like an unsuccessful factory, with two mulberry trees in the front yard.

The teacher was absolutely the meanest bitch I have ever known in my life, nothing pleased her, she snarled and slapped and snorted until everybody in the class was terrified, we worked like dogs. But we didn't seem to learn anything, we just went through the motions, almost hysterical, so of course things got worse and worse. Nothing did any good, you could have cut your throat to please her and she still would have hated your guts. An average schoolteacher, in fact.

And then she started those damn trips of hers. As I remember it, at first we thought it was a terrific idea, anything to get out of that gloomy, hideous building, with its smell of cedar sawdust and stale, infantile pee, we couldn't wait for the first outing. Everybody had to show up in their best clothes that day, washed and combed and buttoned up to the eyeballs, like a Sunday school class. The kids from the other rooms nearly split themselves laughing at us, they thought we were out of our minds and you know nothing gives you such a belly laugh as a real loony walking around in your everyday world. They got a real kick out of it. But for once we didn't give a damn, we were the ones who were getting out, and we piled aboard the bus like we were headed for the Crystal Theater or a calf cutting.

Well, teacher soon fixed that. It was slap, slap, slap, up and down the aisle, pulling ears and twisting cowlicks until we were almost in a panic, ready to kick the windows out. For some reason it never occurred to us to gang her. By the time we pulled up in front of German's Funeral Home everybody's clean clothes had all gone to hell and we were covered with dirt, there was chewing gum in hair and eyebrows and two or three of the more timid souls had wet their pants, including little Robert, of course, he never failed us. We looked like a wild-eyed rabble lined up on the grass in front of the funeral home, like we'd broken out of prison and crawled through a hundred miles of dust to get there, to be on time for the guided tour through the mortuary.

The first thing, of course, was to explain what the hell it was all about. In school we had been reading about the Egyptians and their mummies, the King Tut tomb business happened about that time and it set everybody off, I never knew why. The teacher started brooding about what a stupid bunch we were, I suppose, not understanding embalming and so on, she was sick and tired of trying to explain what it was all about so she decided the hell with it, we'd go to the source. And, too, she probably was just as happy to get out of that damned building as we were, I don't know. Anyway, she lined us up on the grass and tried to make it clear what was about to happen, which was a mistake. Up till then I don't think anybody had any idea what was going on, but as soon as she put it across that we were going in there and look at a lot of dead people the ranks faltered, then broke, and in a split second most of the girls and some of the boys were squawling like turpentined cats. She had a nimble time for a few minutes, running all over the lawn after kids who wanted to go home, hopping around the house, plunging through the canna beds, dodging around among the iron deer and sundials that Mr. German had all over the place. The people passing by must have thought one of our little classmates had kicked off and we had turned up in a group at the funeral, unable to contain our grief. It was lively, but it wasn't getting things done, and pretty soon Mr. German's son came out in his black suit and helped her round up the strays. Little Robert got away, though, he wandered around downtown all that day, wetting his pants every fifteen minutes, until somebody recognized him and took him home. So he missed it.

It was cool inside, but you really couldn't see much. Mr. German's place had been just a house to begin with, the mortuary stuff was all in the basement and the upstairs was pretty much like our own houses, only darker and a good deal tidier, and somehow that made it seem even worse. We trailed around in the gloom in a chorus of little moans, everywhere you looked you could see eyeballs shining. We held on to each other for dear life, and there were squeaks and grunts and sighs and other nervous noises while we were led around through the rooms, completely aimlessly. It was really senseless. Finally the teacher started arguing with Mr. German about letting us go down in the basement where the meat of the matter was, but he refused to do it, he was against the whole idea, in fact, and they had a real go-round while we stood there looking on, waiting for our fate like a bunch of pigs. After a while the teacher gave up and led us back to the bus and we reloaded and went back to school. All we had seen that was unusual was the portable organ and an empty casket, unlined. The rest of it was just rooms and folding chairs, we couldn't understand what the hell it was all about. A field trip!

The next thing was the compress. Naturally we were involved with cotton all the time, no matter what you were studying they always managed to drag cotton into it somehow, and with the Egyptians it was a cinch. As usual, we had to bring bolls of it to school, and we made little speeches about it, the way it had been in every class since we had started school, but you couldn't keep coasting along on your old speeches. Oh, no. Some jerk would snitch if you did that. You had to come up with new facts every year and you had to have a novel way of presenting your cotton boll to the collection, too. We pasted the damn things on cards, we wired them into little trees, we made leis out of them, we dyed them with watercolors, we did every damn thing you can think of with cotton before it was over. Well, of course there was no pleasing this bitch, she didn't think much of our efforts. She flung the silly things back in our faces, she ranted and howled and redoubled her pinching and slapping. We were a spineless bunch, we just took it. She wasn't even reported to the school board by an outraged mother, as far as I know. Of course, she had a lot on her mind, a lot of worries, as it turned out, she probably expected the ax to fall at any minute, but apparently that just made her bear down harder on this cotton business. We'd never had such a siege of it, it made us shudder to think what must be ahead of us in the grades to come. If it was this bad here, what would they expect in junior high school? Would you have to go out and pick the stuff, gin the Goddamned cotton yourself? For Christ's sake! We worried our little heads about it, I can tell you. Little Robert was soaked, every day.

Well, after we'd done everything possible with our bedraggled cotton bolls and had brought in tons of newspaper clippings about it, all smeared around and pasted on cards and in scrapbooks, we had to show up in our best clothes again to go to the compress. The compress! There's not a damned thing to see in one of those places and every kid in town knew it. They pile the cotton in a hopper and a big weight comes down and packs it into a bale. That's all, and you can't even see that, there's always so much dust and lint in the air, and the machinery isn't out where you can stick your finger in it, anyway. A hell of an uproar, but you can't see what they're doing, and if you don't look out one of those tough bastards will knock you on your ear, clear off the loading dock. We all knew that, but we packed ourselves into that stinking bus, a little troop of smelly martyrs, and off we went. We had no guts at all.

The compress manager thought everybody had gone nuts. They'd told him we were coming, all right, but Jesus! A busload, piling out all over the joint! What a day for the compress manager! And the terrible thing for him, of course, was that he couldn't figure out what the hell we were doing there. He'd been around compresses all his life, he didn't see anything unusual about it at all. What else did we expect him to do with the cotton, for God's sake, tie it up with string? Of course they baled it, of course the plunger came down and packed it tight, of course, of course, and we agreed with him. What the hell, we knew all that as well as he did, we weren't idiots, you know. We just stood around and looked at the poor devil, getting filthier by the minute, dirt and lint settling all over us, in our ears, in our nostrils, we could hardly breathe. It was like the rope factory in a prison, and the noise! You couldn't hear yourself scream, so of course we did, we opened our little mouths and bellowed like maddened bulls, looking at the compress manager. To that poor sod it looked like our mouths were hanging open in astonishment at his machine, he couldn't hear a thing. We were all hoarse when we got out of there and nobody had heard us make a sound. That was getting even, all right! That was one up the teacher's nose! We enjoyed that, but it wasn't over yet. She lined us up, the usual business, out in the road this time in dust deeper than our sweaty little ankles, and everybody had to describe what he had just seen. Not just, "They bale cotton." Hell, no! The first one tried that and got a real wallop. You had to go into ecstasies over the crumby place, really tear your heart out about that compress. To be successful at it you needed a degree in hydraulic engineering and a steam boiler operator whispering in your ear. We stood there in the dust and took it, we were absolutely no damned good to Dean Highland school whatsoever. We thought any minute she was going to give us the order to go hop in the compress bin, under the plunger, it was the only honorable way out and we knew it. We were ready, it was tough, but that's the way it was, so what the hell. Let's get it over with. But no, back in the bus, slap, smack, pinch, somebody puking on the floor, a splendid little outing, the teacher behaving like a drunk storm trooper. Well, we've seen the compress, now what. Mass suicide? Why not, what else? There's nothing left, is there? Come on, we'll all do it together, out on the playground. We can hang ourselves from the swing supports, in relays of ten.

Well, that took care of cotton. Let's see, what's next, now. Oh, yes, coffee, of course. Is there anybody here who doesn't know what coffee is? Of course there isn't, we have it all over the house, we practically live on the stuff. Well, that doesn't make a Goddamned bit of difference, you little slobs! What a filthy bunch! What parents you must have! Wipe your noses and get into that bus, or I'll wring every one of your grimy necks! We're going to the coffeeworks.

If anybody else had told us there was a place in town where they ground coffee we wouldn't have believed it. They'd drummed it into us that the stuff came from South America, we knew what the score was. We'd seen a thousand pictures of it growing down there, or over there, or wherever the hell South America was, we'd even seen pictures of it lying on the ground, with people walking around on it barefooted. What the hell! You didn't have to tell us about coffee, we'd all had nightmares about it at some time or other, at one point we had to go around to the grocery stores, begging for a coffee bean to take to class, just to show some teacher we knew what she was talking about. Coffee! Why bother! We weren't even allowed to drink it, yet here it was, coffee, coffee and still more coffee, you heard nothing else. What a world!

They were waiting for us at the coffeeworks, I suppose they were more accustomed to the screwballs in town than the compress manager was, they were a high-class bunch. You'd have thought we were little movie stars, for the first five minues. There we were, all cleaned up again, they thought it was downright sweet. Sweet! Jesus, why didn't they put us to work digging sewers, we were getting a little sick of all this idiocy by now, we were beginning to figure maybe all this wasn't in the contract, that they were putting one over on us, in fact. We hadn't been idle, we'd been asking around.

Well, there it was, the coffee! Now what? There were tons of it, in all stages, and that was all right, we had nothing against it, but so what? Sure, it was coffee, we admitted that, didn't we? What did they want us to do, throw ourselves in it? What good would that do anybody? What was all the fuss about, anyway?

Well, here's the kind they drink in New Orleans, somebody said. See? It's ground up finer than the rest, like powder. New Orleans? What the hell are they talking about? Sure, we supposed they drank coffee in New Orleans, why not, when you think of it? And we dawdled around, an impossible scene. It's really hell in a coffee mill, you know, especially if you don't drink it. Instead of dust in the air you have little motes of coffee, I suppose from the batch those New Orleanians had to have, trying to be different. We figured that out, and we began to hate New Orleans's guts. We breathed the stuff, that powdered coffee filled up our lungs and passed into our bloodstreams until we were as hopped up as if we'd gotten bugged on cocaine. We didn't know what the hell we were doing, it was a colossal coffee jag. Our nerves were shot, we almost got bags under our little eyes, and not one of us slept a wink that night. It upset the whole west end of town. For a week we puked every time we saw a cup of the nasty stuff. We were feverish with caffeine.

Well, that was another one under our belts. Live and let live, that was us, we could stand anything, Powder River, let 'er buck! We hadn't lost anybody yet, we were a damned tough crowd. They were going to have trouble polishing us off, all right. We were ready to go back to the mortuary and start all over again, we'd drag the damn stiffs out in the front yard if we had to, if that was what they wanted. A hardy little class!

We could've kept it up forever, we were just hitting our stride when the whole thing blew up. I got on the streetcar one afternoon and who was sitting in front of me but the teacher, with some woman I'd never seen before. I was on my way down to the Crystal and I didn't want to miss any more of the show than I had already, I just sat there scared stiff, afraid she'd see me and start grilling me about streetcars or electricity or some damn thing. But I got by, she just bawled on the other woman's neck all the way downtown, it was quite a scene, everybody was disgusted, and after that I never saw her again.

The next day we had a new teacher and she had to break the bad news. The old bitch had pinched our little savings, the dough she'd extorted from us a dime at a time so our room would look good on the chart out in the hall, she'd blown the whole seven bucks! Jesus, no! We set up quite an uproar, but there it was, nothing anybody could do about it, we'd just have to lump it. They'd found out about it and fired her, but that didn't get our money back. We wanted her arrested, we wanted the cops to beat hell out of her, but they let her go, of course. That's always the way it is. If *we'd* hooked the seven bucks—brother! They'd have taken us down in the coal bin and buried us alive. But we finally figured, what the hell, you know, at least those idiotic tours were finished with, and just in time. She'd been raving about dragging us out to the cement factory, just before the roof fell in. God knows what would have happened out there, it was a rugged place.

miss euayla is the sweetest thang

⌘ The first day Miss Euayla came into the China Nook, my style just hit her right in the eye. I was dusting off some armadillo baskets when she came in the door and I thought, Lafond T. Cunningham, that's your life mate. Yes, sir. I dropped those baskets and came skipping around the counter and right up to her.

"You sweet *thang!*" I hollered, and went right up on my toes and kissed her on the cheek. You wouldn't believe it, but that's the way I am, impulsive, just impulsive to a fault.

Well, Miss Euayla just stood there a while, looking down at me, neither of us moving an inch, but I could see the feathers in her hat trembling and I just waited her out until finally she just *had* to say something.

"Well," she said. "You sure think you're somebody, don't you."

"That's right," I said, quick as a wink, right back at her. "My name's Lafond T. Cunningham and I'm no bigger than a shotgun."

Well, we just both broke out to laughing until we couldn't see where we were and finally Miss Euayla staggered over and sat down on a wireback chair, whooping and choking until I thought she'd never recover, and I sort of tottered out the door onto the sidewalk, bent over backwards and holding on to my head with both hands, and then I tottered back into the China Nook, my face as red as a dime bandanna. I was screaming like an Indian full of turpentine. We just hit it off right from the start, and all because of my style.

That's just what Rabe Thompson *doesn't* have, of course: my style. I don't care what they say about how good-looking he is, and what if he is six feet tall? He's just a big lump of nothing if you ask me and he got mighty worried as soon as he found out I was seeing Miss Euayla. Thought he *knew* something. Went around telling people I was after Miss Euayla's farm, can you imagine that? Me? Working in the China Nook with a perfectly assured future career ahead of me at that time and don't know a plow from a prunehook. I tried to tell him that the night he hid in my car and tried to scare me silly.

Miss Euayla and me'd been out to the Hickory Rib, sitting in a booth drinking ammonia cokes and playing nickels in the music vendor and that's absolutely all, and about ten o'clock I drove her up into the front yard and parked my '33 Chevie under that big chinaberry tree. We got right out of the car and went in the house and she fixed me a big glass of Kool-Aid, it was hotter than a blister that night, and I came right out of the house and down the steps and bumped into that Chevie before I even saw it. They have darker nights in McClellan County than anywhere in the world, I guess. Well, I got in the car and before I could even step on the starter I feel somebody's breath on the back of my neck and a voice says, "Now I got you!" and without even thinking I let out a holler and started kicking my feet on the floorboards. I like to broke my ankle on the brake pedal, if you want to know the truth. I have very delicate bones.

Well, as soon as I started hollering I heard Miss Euayla start hollering in the house and here she came busting through the screen door and down the steps in the dark like a boxcar of loose roller skates being unloaded.

"Lafond!" she hollered, and ran right into the side of the car. "Damn!" she said, "are you all right?" and right then she sort of grunted and I heard a man's voice say, "Ain't this a fine way to behave? Ain't it?" and it was the same voice that had been talking to me in the car. That scared me so bad I started kicking my feet on the floorboards again so I missed some of what they said, but it was Rabe Thompson hiding out there, waiting and trying to catch us. He and Miss Euayla scuffled around in the dark, both of them cussing and yelling, and Rabe Thompson making out what a skunk I was.

"All he wants is your farm!" he yelled, and Miss Euayla yelled back, "You're a liar! You're a liar!"

It was terrible, the way they kept it up. I rolled up all the windows and locked the doors and nearly suffocated. Every once in a while I'd lean down and holler through the little doors that open up by your feet on those '33 Chevies, but they didn't pay any attention. They'd known each other all their lives, you know. It's a very unhealthy situation, the way people live out in the country, and when they get mad it seems like there isn't anything they won't say to each other, just for spite. Now, growing up in Fort Worth like I did, it's an altogether different thing. You don't have all kinds of people keeping track of you all the time in the city. In Fort Worth it's just plain old "Live and let live." But of course it's not that way down in McClellan County.

That's one reason why, although Miss Euayla was taken with me right from the minute she saw me in the China Nook, she couldn't quite make me out. I just had a different air than anything she was used to, of course, and she couldn't understand why I was working in the China Nook instead of up in Fort Worth in one of the big department stores.

"Why, look here," I told her one night out at the Hickory Rib,

"I'm going to *be* somebody. I'll probably own that old China Nook by next Christmas, armadillo baskets and all."

Miss Euayla took a sip of her dope and just looked at me for a minute.

"How come you couldn't own one of them big stores in Fort Worth by Christmas?" she said after a while.

"That's a different thing and you know it," I told her. "Have another beef sandwich. Sometimes I think you people down here in McClellan County don't understand anything at all."

She just ate her beef sandwich and kept looking at me. Miss Euayla has the worst staring habit of any woman I ever met in my life, and that's a fact. It took me a long time to figure out she was giving me love looks instead of just looking straight through me.

But I'm telling you the honest truth, that night when Rabe Thompson hid in the car just about took ten years off my life. The next day in the China Nook my hands were shaking so bad that I knocked over a whole display of little ceramic Bibles we had piled up there for Easter gifts. They were the cutest things: they had slots in the side where the pages were so you could put money in there and save it up for Sunday school, I suppose. Anyway, Miss Clara, she owns the China Nook, you know, Miss Clara like to died when I knocked them over. I must have busted fifteen of those little Bibles all on account of that Rabe Thompson, and I told Miss Clara so.

"Ha," she said, looking at me with those little beady eyes of hers, just like a weasel looking at a crippled hen. "You better look out, Lafond T.," she said. "That Rabe Thompson's daddy has just about all the money in McClellan County and what he don't have he knows how to lay his hands on it mighty quick," she said. Miss Clara's grammar is just awful. "On top of that," she said, all beady eyes, "they've both of 'em got about the worst tempers in Texas. Why, I can recall when Rabe's daddy was courting his mother," she said, and let off a great string of stories about all the awful things that Mr. Thompson did to boys that were trying to court his future bride at the same time he was. But I just didn't faze, no, sir.

"The pen is mightier than the sword, Miss Clara," I told her, just as chipper as you please. "Might don't always make right, you know. Nowadays a young fellow's got to have brains," I said. "B,r,a,i,n,s."

"Um, hm," Miss Clara said. "Now you sweep up them Bibles."

Honestly! I felt like telling her, Why, no, Miss Clara, I thought I'd just run the Hoover over those little busted up Bibles. Miss Clara, however, is what you might call obtuse. She has absolutely no sense of humor whatever.

Now that was probably very largely responsible for my getting to feel so blue right along in there. I got to thinking that persons that don't have any sense of humor, especially women, live forever, you know; they're the most stubborn things about going off to their just reward that ever was. That's just a plain fact and everybody knows it. Well, here I was, embarked on a dead-end career, when I stopped to think about it.

"It's a burden," Miss Euayla said when I told her about it, but I could see she didn't really understand what I was talking about. The fact of the matter is that Miss Euayla is just the sweetest thing you ever saw for a big girl, but she's pretty short on humor. I guess having her daddy leave her all that money and having to worry about all that cotton makes her that way.

"Yes," I told her, "it is a burden," but I thought, you don't even know what a burden is, you sweet, rich thang, you. "Here I come all the way down to McClellan County from Fort Worth," I told her, "looking for my dear Uncle Dell, and he's flown off somewhere and the first career I pick out for myself, right there in the China Nook, is a big, fat dead end."

"I declare," Miss Euayla said, taking a big bite of beef sandwich. It's a fact, you have to stoke that girl like an ocean liner.

It was the plain truth about my Uncle Dell. I had a letter from him telling me to come on down and join up with him in something good, and when I got to McClellan County all I could find out was that he'd run off somewhere in a 1929 Pierce Arrow touring sedan. Bright red. Everybody said he went to California, but he wouldn't wait for me, oh, no. Selfish, just plain selfish.

"How'm I ever going to get ahead?" I said. "I'll have to cast about for a new career."

Miss Euayla polished off her sandwich and looked at me.

"How about Rabe's daddy's compress," she said. "Maybe he'd give you a job."

Well, I laughed so hard I like to fell out of the booth.

"Me?" I said. "Lafond T. Cunningham stalking around a cotton compress, breathing all that fuzz and listening to all that racket?"

"You're afraid of Rabe," Miss Euayla said, looking around in that puzzled fashion that means she wants another beef sandwich.

"Oh, no you don't!" I hollered. "You're not going to pin that label on a Cunningham!" I told her, but she waved her hand at the waitress.

"You've no call to be afraid of Rabe," she said, looking at me again.

"Oh, no?" I said. "Not that I am, mind you, but if I don't have any call to be afraid of him, what you come running out of the house that way that night? When he hid in the car and tried to scare me into my grave, I mean."

"That was different," she said. "It was dark. It ain't dark around a compress."

Well, I just wanted to scream, or hit her over the head with that little pile of sandwich plates she had stacked in front of her.

"*Isn't* dark," I said. "Not *ain't*."

"All right," she said.

I could see I wasn't going to make Miss Euayla understand economics in a hurry, and I wasn't *about* to go to work in a cotton compress, and certainly not in one where Rabe Thompson could get hold of me. Like I say, I have very delicate bones, it's a part of the Cunningham style, and a cotton compress is like all hell's broken loose in an insane asylum. Noise? That's where they invented noise. I have no doubt that three or four people get killed each and every day in Texas cotton compresses. I decided maybe I'd go on the radio.

That's one nice thing you can say for the radio, it's clean work, and if you don't like the noise you can put on some of those headphone things and just look interested without even turning the thing on while you sit right in the studio where they're making the racket. I've seen them do that in the movies, you know. It's sort of like being deaf and turning down the volume on your hearing aid: that's why so many deaf people have such sweet smiles, my Uncle Dell always said, and I believe it.

Well, I called up Miss Clara on the telephone next morning and told her I had a sick headache and was going to stay in bed all day with wet teabags on my eyes. There was just a humming kind of silence for a while, and then she hung up. The rudest old party you ever ran across.

I put on my checkered suit and my black and white perforateds and strutted right on down to the radio station, carrying my guitar in a yellow pillow slip. I've had that box for years: it was left to me, but some jealous person or other stole the case a long while ago. I'm not going to name any names, you understand: whoever did it knows he did it, and I don't think the entire city of Fort Worth is big enough to hold his guilty conscience. Envy is a terrible thing.

But anyway. In the radio station there was this dangerous-looking blonde behind the counter and she let me right on in to see Mr. Big himself. When I opened the door to his office I had the pillow slip off the guitar and folded up and stuck in my pocket, and I went right into my act.

"Yes, sir!" I said, skipping through the door. "I'm the biggest little singer west of the Sabine River!" and with that I lit right into the opening of "I Want to Live Fast, Love Hard, Die Young and Leave a Beautiful Memory."

Well, that man was stunned. He just sat there behind his desk looking at me, and his mouth got open wider and wider until you could have driven a team of mules through his dentures and right out again and I don't think he'd have known a thing.

Of course I hadn't been getting much exercise in the China Nook and I was breathing pretty hard when I hit the last chord. I pulled the pillow slip out of my pocket and dabbed at my face with it, at the same time giving him a stylish little bow, with the guitar flung off to one side in my left hand and my left foot out and pointed. Style! If there's one thing I know about, it's style.

"How do you like that for a starter?" I said, puffing a little, and the man closed his mouth.

"If you'd just wait in the outer office," he said, still sitting there looking at me.

"Certainly!" I cried. "Make it easy on yourself!" and I did a quick off-to-Buffalo back out where the blonde was and sat down on a bench to get my breath. The air in McClellan County is as heavy as lead: you'd think you were in Death Valley all the time.

They had a radio going in there and a man was talking about the biggest discovery in the scientific world since the atom bomb, he said. I wasn't paying too much attention, but I began to make out that he was talking about Hollywood Synthetic Diamond Rings. You could send off for them, like something out of the Ivor Johnson catalogue, and they were absolutely guaranteed. Well, I surely was surprised. I started to listen pretty hard but I heard Mr. Big's voice, talking in his office over the telephone and it sounded urgent, like on Dragnet.

"He's crazy as a bedbug," I heard him say. "You better get somebody down here right away." There was a little pause and he said, "Sure, he's dangerous! You ought to see him! He looks like a

June bug peeking out from behind a chrysanthemum when he starts to waving that yellow pillowcase around!"

Well, I had to admit it, he was talking about me! I've never been so shocked in my life, nor so insulted. I just marched right out of there and went back to my room and sat right down and wrote off a letter to the Hollywood Synthetic Diamond people and then went down to the post office and stuck a four ninety-five money order in it and mailed it. I was sick and tired of fooling around. If you ask me a person can stand just so much. The Lord helps those who helps themselves, you know, you can't just stand around hoping to get a leg up on somebody else's bootstraps, or whatever it is.

After I mailed off the letter I went back to my rooming house and changed my clothes and went out back and polished up that '33 Chevie until it squeaked when you looked at it. The finish had a shine like a raven's wing in the sunlight: a lot of the black was a little worn off on places and looked sort of bluish-black and green. Just beautiful. But of course that's just about the hardest work a man can do. I had to go upstairs and lay down for a while with a magazine. If you want a good workout, go down to McClellan County and polish a '33 Chevie some afternoon. I was too tuckered to talk.

But it passed off after I'd had my lie-down, of course. I got up and telephoned Miss Euayla.

"I'm going to have some mighty big news before long for you," I told her, in spite of the fact I wasn't too certain yet myself what it was going to be.

"What are you going to do," she said after a minute, sounding so faint and far away and distracted I could tell she was hungry and looking around her living room for something to eat. "You going to work in the compress?"

"You just stop that," I said. "Fortune might turn my way at any time, Miss Smarty. You'll see."

"All right," she mumbled with her mouth full, and hung up.

Some people just don't know destiny when it walks up and hits them in the face.

But I made it a little plainer next day. Miss Euayla came in the China Nook looking for a wedding present for someone of her cotton-headed cousins out in the country, and I fired my arrow.

"I'm going to be looking for a wedding present myself one of these days," I told her. "For my bride."

Miss Euayla looked at me, then back at the ceramic frog flower holder she was weighing in her hand.

"You can't ever tell," I said. "One of these days!"

"I think I'll send them this," Miss Euayla said, handing me the frog.

"You ought to give a party for that barefooted cousin of yours," I told her as I wrapped up the frog in a big wad of pink tissue paper. "A big engagement party of some kind."

"Mm," Miss Euayla said, blinking at me. "That's what Rabe thinks, too."

"Oh, does he!" I hollered. "Well, maybe he's got some ulterior motive or other. Me, I just like to see folks have a good time. There's little enough that's jolly in this old world."

"Mm, hm," Miss Euayla said. "That's what Rabe thinks."

"Well, then, go on and give your old party!" I said, hopping up and down a little. I was so put out I was furious, but anyway she was going to have the party and as soon as she left the China Nook I could see that was all that mattered. I have too much pride, I guess I know that as well as anybody does, and temperament, too, it just seems to go with talent.

Miss Euayla even put it in the paper about the party. She sent out little bids to it, all printed up, inviting the bearer to be present at the Fish Pond, which is the ridiculous name they have in McClellan County for that splintered old shack they call a country club. They don't even have a pond. There's nothing out there but an old stagnant ox-bow lake, and if you don't look out you can step right through the clubhouse floor and fall in the water. Society!

Well, anyway, the great day dawned, as they say in the classics. I had my plot all ready, but I was nearly taken off in a fit, waiting for the Hollywood Diamond people to come through. I didn't get the package until three p.m., I'll have you know, and if I hadn't been right there when the postman came up the front porch steps I probably never would have gotten it. That landlady of mine was the nosiest old blister you ever saw. I just ran right by her with that package and right on up the stairs, with her hollering down at the foot, "What's that you got, Lafond? You sent off for something through the mail?"

"That's for me to know and you to find out!" I hollered back, just sassed her good, and went into my room and opened the package.

It just plain took your breath away. That Hollywood Diamond was as big around as a bottle cap. I held the ring over by the window in the light and it just snapped and sparkled, just sat right up and looked you in the eye. It wasn't even cracked, after coming all the way from Hollywood, which I guess is about as far from McClellan County as a person could get without a passport. Just beautiful! I gave that diamond a good burst with some patented window cleaner I kept in there for my dresser mirror and rubbed it on my sleeve and my, heavens! you could hardly stand to look at it.

It took me the rest of the afternoon to get dressed. My checkered suit hadn't even hardly got rumpled at the radio station so I wore that and a new pink shirt I'd been saving to go off with Uncle Dell in, if he ever showed up. And my perforateds, of course: even after my radio audition they were still in A number one shape, I'm that careful of myself, you know.

So, there I was. When I came downstairs the landlady, Miss Vandy, came out to devil me some more about that package but when she saw me she was just speechless. She stared at me for a good minute without saying a thing.

"Take a good look," I told her. "You're looking at a young man on the threshold," I said. "How do you like my cravat?"

Miss Vandy swallowed a couple of times and nodded.

"You're just a picture, Lafond," she said. "Just a picture."

"That's vanadium green," I said, shaking my cravat at her.

"A beautiful necktie," she said. "Just beautiful. Are you off to a wedding?"

"No, Miss Nosey!" I said, "nor to a hanging, either!" and with that I skipped out the screen door, flip! flap! "I'll tell you when it's wedding time!" I hollered back over my shoulder.

Everybody in the world was out at the Fish Pond. Cars, you never saw so many cars, and Japanese lanterns strung up and down the veranda. There was a crowd at the water doing a lot of yelling and swearing, because of course somebody had already driven off the bank in the dark. That happens at least once every time there's a party out there. I just hoped it was Rabe Thompson, with his mouth full of live catfish.

I parked that '33 Chevie and even at night it had a shine on it from the lanterns up on the veranda. There was not a thing in the world about that car to be ashamed of. I closed the door gently just to hear the sound: I had the insides of the doors sprayed with asphalt up in Fort Worth. There's a place up there that does things like that and the man who runs it told me that's what they do on all those big new cars in Detroit. It's quite the thing, he said, and it surely gives the door a nice tone when it shuts: expensive.

I tiptoed up to the veranda, trying to keep my perforateds from getting absolutely soaked by the dew, because they either have dew in McClellan County at night or frost. It's always one or the other and of course all that moisture just plays hob with two-tone shoes. I finally got up to the door, bent over and gave my footgear a quick flick with my handkerchief and then flew into the ballroom, skipping for all I was worth.

"Where's that lucky couple!" I hollered, skipping through that great roil of people like a fresh breeze. I could see Miss Euayla's hat sticking up away over yonder in the corner where they keep the nickelodeon so I just bent my course in that direction and pretty soon I busted out of the dancers right in front of her.

She had one of those little canvas sacks in her hand that you use to take the money to the bank in, and she was fishing nickels out of it and stuffing them into the music box. They never seem to be able to put the vendor on automatic down there, somebody has to stand there and feed it, and usually it's the hostess. Just no savoir faire in the whole county. That's French.

"My dear madame," I said, giving her that deep bow of mine, foot pointed, arm flung out to one side, the whole works. "You *are* the sweetest *thang*," I said, "and you are mine tonight!"

"Hello, Lafond," Miss Euayla said, looking up from that grubby sackful of nickels. She looked at me, just taking me in for a minute. "Where'd you get that necktie?" she said finally.

"This is a cravat," I told her. "When you pay two and a half for a necktie, it's a cravat. Vanadium green," I told her. "That's a mineral color."

"Mm, hm," she said. "It looks more like a vegetable color. Kind of spinach."

"Just rave on, my girl," I told her, haughty as could be, "Just enjoy yourself. You are looking at a man of the world, that's all, if you only had sense enough to see it. Fortune has finally smiled."

"Mm, hm," Miss Euayla said. "What'd you do, get another job?"

"Job!" I cried. "You are looking at a Cunningham of independent means. I just got the word today."

"Word?" Miss Euayla looked at that sack of nickels, then back at me. I could tell I had her curiosity up or she'd have gone on fishing out nickels.

"About my Uncle Dell," I said. "That poor, rich man. He's had a terrible accident in that big red Pierce Arrow of his, out in

Hollywood. Ran into some big movie star or other and killed them both outright. I forget the other fellow's name."

"For heaven's sake," she said.

"Just awful," I said, "and now he's left me so much money I don't know what to do with it. Probably be even more cash later. I'm going to sue that other fellow's estate, of course."

"Is that a fact," Miss Euayla said, looking at me.

Well, it could have been, you know. The important thing in this life is to think big, if you want to be big. Of course I knew the time would have to come when I'd be bound to explain a few things to Miss Euayla, but that would be after we were welded together in the sanctity of marriage.

"Just rich as a black marketeer," I told her. "And look here what I got you today," and I hauled that big sparkler out of my pocket and slipped it on her finger before you could say scat.

"What on earth," Miss Euayla said, while I shoved and pushed on that ring until we both of us like to fell crash into the juke box. The ring was too little to go on her ring finger, I finally saw that after huffing and puffing around for a while, so I put it on her little finger, but it wouldn't go there, either. Honestly! You can't trust anybody at all, not even the diamond trust. I shoved it back on her ring finger but it stuck out there on the first joint, just wouldn't go past that first knuckle.

While all that was going on Miss Euayla forgot to keep stuffing that music box with nickels and it was good and quiet when I stepped back from her and made my announcement.

"There!" I said, flinging out my arms like I was on a stage. "You are bound to Lafond T. Cunningham for life, you big sweet thang, you!" but there was a kind of a roar behind my back.

I looked around and here came Rabe Thompson, roaring like a wounded mastodon, all covered with mud from trying to get some fool's car out of the water, just dripping and squishing across the dance floor like a creature from out of the wet past.

"No, you ain't!" he trumpeted at Miss Euayla. "You ain't bound to nobody but me!" and he commenced to fumbling in his pockets with those muddy hams of his until he finally dredged out a little blue box no bigger than a carbuncle and snapped it open in front of Miss Euayla's face.

Well, it was just laughable. There was a little bitty old ring in there, sort of gold colored with a stone in it about the size of the head on a kitchen match.

"Now, look at that!" I said, striking a pose with my hands on my hips. "Did you ever see such a piker? Just you take a good big fat look at that ring I just slipped on that girl's finger!" I told him, and he did.

"I ain't going to stand for it!" he roared in that big undignified voice of his, and he grabbed my ring off Miss Euayla's finger tip and hurled it, just hurled it, down on the floor.

Now, a lot of people wouldn't believe this, but it's just the kind of luck I had up there in McClellan County all the time. That diamond ring just exploded when it hit the floor, just flew into a million pieces and scattered all over. We all just stood there for a second, and then Rabe Thompson let out a great bellow.

"That ain't no diamond ring!" he shouted at Miss Euayla. "He's trying to take advantage of you just like I said he would! He's after your cotton!" and he made a grab for me, but I slipped away just as nimble as you please and went running for the door. Just before I took off I noticed the strangest thing: Miss Euayla had a big fat grin on her face and I don't believe she was paying any attention at all. Isn't that the most peculiar thing you ever heard of in your entire life?

But I didn't have time to think about it, I just made for the door, with Rabe Thompson right after me.

"You're a liar!" I told him over my shoulder. We went through that door like the locomotive and the coal car on the Bluebonnet Special, both of us yelling for all we were worth. I don't recall hearing Miss Euayla's voice at all.

It was quite a chase, just like something in the first part of a

Doug Fairbanks picture, with me playing Doug Fairbanks, of course. Up hill, down dale, hither and thither, you might say, just screaming through the night.

Well, I finally shook him on the edge of town and doubled back out to the Fish Pond and got my car. I didn't even bother to go back to my rooming house to pick up my things. There's no telling what an animal type like that Rabe Thompson might do, you know: just watch him any afternoon in the week, swaggering around down on the square in his daddy's pickup truck. No, sir, I just headed straight south and here I am.

I've been here in Galveston two weeks now, with this *very* pleasant job handing out bathing suits in Murdoch's Swimming Pavillion, and any day now I'm going to contact Miss Euayla for the good news. She doesn't know my exact whereabouts, you understand, or of course she'd have gotten in touch already. I just know she's going to tell me she's run that Rabe Thompson off for good and that she wants me to hop right back up there, quick as a wink. Absence makes the heart grow fonder, you know, and my style just shows off even better this way, at this point in time, sort of aloof and withdrawn down here on the edge of this dirty old Gulf of Mexico, just sending off an occasional little love note up there to McClellan County. And there's no two ways about it, most of those cotton-heads up there never even heard of the Gulf of Mexico, much less ever saw it, and I just leave it to you to guess how glamorous that old Galveston postmark will look to Miss Euayla. Just one of those little things, but you add them all up and you've got style, and that's just me, Lafond T. Cunningham.

the fishers: 1932

::   After Mr. Fisher lost his job as a brakeman on the Katy he bought a second-hand Chevrolet sedan and drove it as a dime taxi for a while, but there wasn't enough money in it, so he decided he would make pies.

Nobody in the neighborhood knew why he happened to think of pies; nobody asked, and he didn't say. Mr. Fisher wasn't a friendly man. He was big, brakeman-sized, and his neck was red and scaly. It was said he once killed a hobo with the brake club like a baseball bat he used to turn the boxcar brake wheels; he hadn't meant to kill him, but he was loyal to the Katy; he knew his duty.

The Fishers were the only family in the neighborhood which dealt with Sears & Roebuck through the mail. There were three Fisher sons: Homer, seventeen; Weldon, twelve, and Raymond, eight, but the packages were never for them. The first thing Mr. Fisher ordered from the catalogue was a set of cobbler's tools for repairing the family shoes. There were five pairs of iron feet on little columns out in the back-yard shed, diminishing in size from Mr. Fisher's mighty sole to Raymond's little one and even after the iron feet were too small for the boys Mr. Fisher still used them. It didn't seem to make much difference.

After the cobbler's tools Mr. Fisher bought a huge steam pressure cooker for Mrs. Fisher to use for canning. It stood in a corner of the screened-in back porch when not in action, like a nickel-plated kettledrum. And then came a set of barber shears and scissors to cut the family hair and an ugly apparatus of black iron which seized a tire and spread it open so Mr. Fisher could work on the inside of the casing with his repair kit. He bought all these things while he was still a brakeman on the Katy, before times got tough, as though he knew it was going to be like that and was getting ready to hold out as long as he could.

The equipment for the pies was the most elaborate of all. There were four square ovens, with stern, heavy handles on the front like those on a locomotive's firebox door; there were deep metal tubs to do the mixing in, and great steel baking sheets dented to hold dozens of pies. The pies were the nickel size which was very popular at that time. Mr. Fisher fitted the back of the sedan with wooden racks where the finished pies rested in paper plates during delivery, and he was in business.

It was a family undertaking, conceived in silent desperation, and the only one who enjoyed it was Raymond. He was very religious then, a member of the Baptist Young People's Union at the Highland Baptist Church a block away, and he liked carrying the little pies back and forth. He wanted to be a preacher someday.

Homer was the mean one, everybody said: he was always making trouble. He hated the pie-making; he bought a five-dollar guitar and a set of lessons and told everybody he wanted to be a cowboy on the radio. Mr. Fisher didn't like it; he whipped him until he got too big, and after that he would refuse to let Homer into the house some nights when he came home late. They used to wake up the whole neighborhood.

Homer found a job in a poolroom down on the square and in

the afternoons, when the pie-making was at its highest pitch, he would open the door of the bedroom where he slept with his brothers and run down the hall and out the back door before his father could catch him. Then he would lean against the screen door while his father tried to push it open, both of them cursing at each other and shouting until you could hear it clear down at Hardin's Grocery. The family never used the front door at all.

After a while Mr. Fisher would have to go back to his pies and Homer would walk around the house and down the driveway to the street, combing his hair, which he greased with Crisco every day. He had a pointed, mean face like a weasel, with beady little eyes like a weasel, and he carried a snap-open knife with a four-inch blade in his pocket. In the summertime the Crisco would start to run before he got to the car line and he would stand there, mopping his forehead with a dirty handkerchief, darting his little eyes around like he was in Chicago or St. Louis, waiting for the streetcar like a weasel in a tight, twelve-dollar suit. He didn't act like a cowboy at all.

Weldon didn't say much; he wanted to be just like Homer. Raymond despaired of him, screamed at him out in the garage as they loaded pies into the sedan, wept over him. There were dozens of empty one-gallon mineral-oil jars stacked around the base of the garage walls and Raymond had to be careful when he was screaming at Weldon or they got knocked over and broken. Mr. and Mrs. Fisher both suffered from chronic constipation; it was their only luxury. They consumed surprising amounts of mineral oil from Sears & Roebuck and every few months Mr. Fisher returned the empties for a refund.

Nobody in the neighborhood ever tasted one of Mr. Fisher's pies. They were never given away nor eaten at home, and people in the neighborhood never went into the places which bought the pies from Mr. Fisher. They were artificial-looking confections, with a broad cone of grainy, hard meringue on top, like plaster. It was impossible to see what was inside, under the meringue, but there were all kinds of fillings: some days it was coconut, other times banana cream or pecan, and always they were a nickel each and quite durable; they held up for days on the counters of the restaurants where Mr. Fisher sold them.

Every day after school Raymond and Weldon worked with their parents, making the pies, but they never ate any. The pies were ammunition, and not to be fired off at random; the enemy was on the porch, fingering the doorknobs; every round must count. After all, Mr. Fisher's pies retailed for a nickel each; he had to sell them for three cents. As the country slowed, grumbled and fell silent, he was out in the sedan all day long, not coming home until nine or ten o'clock at night sometimes, and once he drove clear to Temple, twenty-five miles away, trying to get the bus station there to handle his pies, but they wouldn't do it. And every day Raymond and Weldon would start to work as soon as they got home, mixing, carrying pies to the roaring ovens and from the ovens to the racks, washing the tubs and steel sheets amid clang and clatter. There was always something to do. The light over the back door burned late every night, and the slap-slap of the screen could be heard when others were in bed, for not everyone chose to fight 1932 in this fashion.

When they were finally finished for the night Mr. and Mrs. Fisher would go into their bedroom at the front of the house and Raymond and Weldon would go into their room at the back. Weldon shared a bed with Homer, but he was always asleep by the time the poolhall employee came home. Raymond had a canvas army cot to himself, and after he undressed except for his underwear he would sit on the cot and look at the colored Bible pictures the preacher gave him, talking about them to Weldon, trying to get him interested.

But, "I'm on git me a *git*-tar," Weldon would interrupt in his dull voice, and he would look at Homer's pillow, covered with the dark splotches the Crisco made, and that would make Raymond mad.

"No, you ain't, neither," he would say firmly, pursing his lips and looking at his brother. "You ain't gone do no such of a thing." He was eight years old and the preacher had told him that before too long he would become a real member of the church. "We gone buy seeds with that money," he would say, although there was no money, "and one uh them little plows with a wheel on her," for there was a picture of a proud, compact little garden plow in the catalogue and Raymond wanted a garden in the back lot, so they need no longer buy vegetables from Hardin's Grocery. "*He* won't leave you buy no *git*-tar, anyways."

"Mama on make him," Weldon would answer, still looking at the Crisco spots, and Raymond would sigh with exasperation and put his pictures away in a shoebox, then go to bed. It wasn't easy for a BYPU member in this house.

Mrs. Fisher frequently made promises to Weldon and Homer but never to Raymond, since he never asked her for anything. She was a silent woman who never left the house, a small, female version of Homer's weaselness, shuffling from room to room in red felt bedroom slippers. Like her husband, she came from a family of cotton sharecroppers, one of many children born to a dark, brooding couple of no education and apparently less imagination, whose children, the sons and daughters of the pioneers, resembled them exactly. She had never understood town ways and had no curiosity about them, nor had Mr. Fisher, although his work on the Katy and then with the pies took him out into the town every day. They were suspicious of it, not seeing it as merely an extension, a distillation of the cotton farmers who surrounded it, and so Mrs. Fisher never went out into it at all and Mr. Fisher did so narrowly, almost blindly, unaware of gossip or humor or politics, never even reading the paper. People who passed on the sidewalk in front of the house often saw Mrs. Fisher peering at them around the drawn windowshade in her bedroom, and if they were neighbors and went to the back door on some neighbor business she talked to them through the screen, saying as little as was necessary for the business but not unfriendly and even letting them into the house if the business made that necessary, but she never called at the other back doors in the neighborhood. The neighbors did not consider her especially remarkable or eccentric, however; they were accustomed to such people. At that time there were Fishers in every neighborhood, all over the town.

However, in one respect this particular Mr. Fisher, this former brakeman for the Katy railroad, was regarded as strangely out of character, above the normal run of Fishers: he was not a drinking man. The town's Fishers, and certainly the brakemen on the Katy, were whiskey drinkers; it set them apart like their overalls and pointed felt hats, forced into that strange, witches' shape on broom sticks, while the felt was wet. The other people in the town drank home brew which they concocted in their garages. And even that was primarily for summer use, although there were exceptions, of course; but the town's Fishers drank illegal whiskey the whole year 'round; it eased them.

But not the silent, pie-making Mr. Fisher. It was considered odd, a little too respectable; it bordered on sanctimonious display. And yet, Mr. Fisher did not attend the Highland Baptist Church nor any other church. He swore, and violently; he was as vulgar as his antecedents. He broke wind in front of his family or even among the lady shoppers in Hardin's Grocery, if he felt like it; after all, what difference did it make? And always he was dark and sullen, like those violent ancestors, dissatisfied and vaguely resentful, unarmed against his enemy. Not a churchman at all.

But, there it was: he was not a drinking man. He abhorred it. When Homer came home drunk at the age of fourteen his father beat him with his broad, stout belt, a piece of leather as heavy and stiff as harness. After that Homer did not come home drunk; he stayed away until he was sober, vomiting in the distempered men's room of the Phoenix Café on the square.

And women; Mr. Fisher warned Homer about women in such

filthy language that it seemed impossible he had ever married, that
he had ever brought himself in contact with the diseased, grasping, lying tribe and produced Homer, Weldon and Raymond.
When Raymond heard his father lecturing Homer in this way it
drove him to furious tears, he would rush out of the house with
angry cries and sit in the garage or the shed which joined it,
sobbing and promising himself holy vengeance against Mr. Fisher;
he prayed that his huge, monstrous parent would be delivered into
his hands for righteous, wrathful punishment of the Old Testa-
ment variety. And then Mr. Fisher would shout his name and it
would be time to start working on the pies and Raymond would go
back to his labor, his face stained with tears and dirt and cobwebs.
At such times he worked frenziedly, rallying Weldon with fierce
shouts, darting from the ovens to the racks in the sedan, scrubbing
pans like a small wild man. It seemed that he hoped to outwit his
father's vulgarity (although he did not know it as such) with this
family labor, this community effort against charity, and in exact
proportion to the humbling of his father, to do homage to his
mother, that peering, shuffling, weasel-faced woman, member of
the caste which Homer was warned to beware. Mother, and little
Jesus, and the evil men!

Homer, of course, found girls: a succession of waitresses from
the Phoenix Café or others like it, places that were dim, smelling
of chili and long-dead grease, with corrugated iron awnings over
the sidewalk out front; or girls from the pecan factory, they who
worked in stifling heat in summer and not at all in winter since
the pecans come in hot weather, girls in loose blue cotton smocks
shelling mountains of pecans, carefully picking the meats out
whole since broken ones were forfeit in the day's poundage score,
their fingers stained a light brown, like Homer's own nicotined
fingers. He took them to the Cotton Palace park in summer, and
in winter (in the battered, rattling old Ford of a friend) to
unpainted farmhouses out in the country, where whiskey was sold.
Finally, inevitably, he found one he loved, a Dolores or Rosemary

or Dot, and he frequently displayed his four-inch knife in the farmhouse fights, defending the one he had chosen from speech like his own but which was not to be tolerated because it was not his own, and then, equally finally, inevitably, he wanted to bring the girl to the house while Mr. Fisher was away. He told his mother he wanted to have friends at the house for a party.

Mrs. Fisher, not understanding, since this was something she knew nothing of, agreed to plot with him against Mr. Fisher. There was no question of revealing the plan to the husband and father; they refused even to think of such a disaster. Therefore the party must take place in the afternoon, while Mr. Fisher was abroad in town, selling his pies, and must be ended, the guests gone, at a safe hour.

At first Mrs. Fisher was pleasantly stirred by the idea of Homer's party, then frightened. It roused her from the patient, unquestioning gloom in which she unwittingly lived; it was the unknown, the intangible, qualities she perhaps had known in childhood but never since, for in the Fisher household intangibles were not considered, they did not exist in any consciousness save possibly Raymond's nor did any mind other than his dwell on the unknown. Conversation between parents and children was short, monosyllabic, and always of the immediate present. It had been so in the home of her own parents and Mrs. Fisher was not aware that it could or should be otherwise. But now Homer's plan shook her, she felt for the first time that he was "different," that he was moving forward and away from her blood, from something considered normal until now toward something indefinably better, and she was glad he had found his job in the poolroom, among the town people he understood and valued, the restless, active, talky town people. Change (so dreaded, so unwanted, always so near in 1932) must in this matter be good, and her mind moved slowly, unevenly, stiff with disuse, over this aspect of her son and his life in the poolroom on the square, unknown, but so suddenly present and requiring action.

She was not sure what was to make this party but she did not
ask Homer. He had told her what he wanted: a party, since other
people had them; she had agreed and he had gone off to his
poolroom. She might have conceived of it and even tried to form
it on some vague remembrance of a country funeral or wedding,
with the men in the yard and the women in the kitchen, if
Raymond had not sensed her mistake and corrected it.

"You on have ice cream?" he asked, looking up at her. "That's
what they have at BYPU parties."

Mrs. Fisher looked down at him with her beady, weasel eyes,
duller eyes than Homer's but unmistakably animal-like, wild fear
and hate hidden behind the dullness and dumb patience.

"Mm," she said, looking down at her youngest son.

"And one uh them white cakes," Raymond said. "With green
ice cream. They can sit in the front room and play the radio."

So it was decided, and on the appointed day Raymond took the
limp dollar his mother gave him and walked to Hardin's Grocery,
where he bought a white cake packaged in cardboard and cellophane and a quart of lime ice cream. Then he walked home and
gave his mother the change from the dollar, put the ice cream in
the icebox, the cake on the kitchen table, combed his hair with
water and sat down in the kitchen to wait for Homer's party.
Weldon stood at a window in the front room and Mrs. Fisher
posted herself behind her bedroom windowshade. They peered
around the shades, watching for Homer's arrival. Raymond sat in
the kitchen, reading his BYPU magazine with thudding heart,
longing yet fearful, and Mr. Fisher was in a Mexican café, staring
heavily at the counter while he waited for the proprietor to buy or
reject his pies, ignoring the rapid, spattering Spanish tongues and
the smells of tacos, chili pepper sauce and fried rice, thinking
about his old job on the Katy and how well he had performed
in it.

Weldon grunted and ran into his mother's bedroom.

"They comin'," he said. "They in a car," raising the shade in front of his mother before she could stop him and she saw a Ford roadster, rakish and battered, turning into the yard.

"Here!" she said, jerking down the shade, and she raised her arm as though she would strike Weldon. She looked at him, then shuffled into the front room and sat down on the sofa, getting up at once to turn on the radio and then return to the sofa. Weldon took the chair by the radio and they sat silently, not moving, not looking at each other, their hands on their thighs as the radio hummed, warming up. They heard the metallic slam of the car doors in the back yard and then the slap of the screen door and voices in the kitchen, coming down the hall, and Homer entered the front room followed by another boy and two girls. The radio hummed powerfully and a man's voice started talking about Purina feeds.

For perhaps ten seconds after the foursome entered the room Mrs. Fisher and Weldon could smell them. There was a stale, rancid odor about them, of grease-impregnated clothing hung too long in a closed closet, the smell of a bed which has not been made for days or weeks, but it faded quickly into the usual close, almost fetid smell of the house and the room's first occupants thought nothing of it. Mrs. Fisher did not look at the young people when she was introduced to them by Homer in a quick, unfinished way, nor did she speak. She continued to sit with her hands on her thighs, her slippered feet close together, gazing steadily and calmly at the wall. She looked small on the bright blue plush of the sofa, and when the girls sat down on each side of her the cushions rose under her, lifting her feet from the floor. She paid no attention. Weldon, following his mother's example or stiff with self-consciousness, sat as he had before, staring straight ahead as though he had been falsely accused of a crime and was not going to talk about it any more. Homer and the other boy leaned against the wall, glowering about them at the furniture, the radio and Weldon. Wooden matchsticks dangled from their lips like gangster cigarettes and their movements were queerly alike; they moved a hand from pocket to matchstick rapidly as it left the pocket then slowed it as it reached the matchstick, slowing it insolently, provocatively, until the fingers took the matchstick delicately and probed the teeth with it. No one spoke. The Purina man talked enthusiastically into the room, his voice rolling jovially, full of promise, over the silent Fishers, the strange boy and the fat-faced, thick-lipped girls, sitting stiffly with their hands holding glittering patent leather purses in their laps.

Then, from nerves or from habit, since it was something she did frequently every day, a symptom, perhaps, of that condition which drove her to such huge, clotted draughts of mineral oil, Mrs. Fisher belched, a rasping, mannish noise which ripped the air like a power saw slicing a plank, and instantly, following immediately in the sound, Weldon, screwed to such high tension as he had never known before and gaseous from the starchy Fisher diet of 1932, broke wind. His face turned scarlet at once but he did not change his position; his expression settled more firmly into that of the badgered, innocent youth, held incommunicado and for no reason whatever in the city jail.

Homer's friend giggled, a wet snicker which seemed to come from his acne-pocked nose, and the girls tittered, but it was plain that all three were laughing kindly and indulgently at Mrs. Fisher's explosion, not Weldon's. They ignored his action, it was not something to laugh at in front of somebody else's mother, whereas the belch was nothing but a comical, ordinary thing, an idiosyncrasy of age; possibly Mrs. Fisher had done it to be enter-taining. They chided her gently with their giggles, relieved to find she was human instead of merely Homer's mother, and did not acknowledge Weldon's behavior although in a short time, as soon as they were released from the company and implied influ-ence of another generation, they would speak of it as wonderfully comic while they felt it as a sexual joke, since it reminded them of many things. Thus even Weldon's mishap was not without value and significance. Its implications were deep and exciting; like Homer's pocketknife, it had an aphrodisiacal quality, although of doubtful necessity, since they already possessed whiskey rights and twenty-five cent motion pictures.

Mrs. Fisher was uncertain about the actions of Weldon and herself in relation to the strangers, but she didn't dwell on it. She felt the need for conversation rather than thought, the need to impress directly upon these visitors the warning that she was a being, Homer's mother, in fact, and so she turned to him.

"He'll whup you to death when he finds out," she said in a flat, matter-of-fact tone.

Homer looked startled; for an instant he imagined something had gone wrong, that his father had learned of the party and forced the complicity of Mrs. Fisher, Weldon and Raymond in setting a dreadful trap for him. He pictured Mr. Fisher lurking in the garage or the shed, big, solid and dangerous in his blue overalls, biding his time. But the vision and the fear passed quickly; he realized his mother's intent, that of self-assertion in the only way she knew: the threat, the hint of a catastrophe in which she would not be implicated and on which she would not bother to pass judgment (although in this case she was certain to be involved in any mischance, she would stand or fall with Homer whether she willed it or not, since she was now hopelessly committed) and he understood it, because he used the device himself.

"Oh, yeah?" he said, curling his lips around the matchstick. "He ain't never gone touch *me* no more," and he glared at his friends, as though it were they who threatened him. He narrowed his eyes and twisted his lips painfully farther, he hunched his shoulders up and forward in a gesture of aggressive defense; he tried very hard to look as he felt a young man with a four-inch blade in his pocket should look.

"*That* old fool," he said.

"You hush your mouth now," said Mrs. Fisher, but she had lost interest; her eyes turned from Homer back to the wall. Her old feeling of numbness, of dumb, undirected patience was settling back on her, there seemed no reason to impress these people with her existence after all; she had established her familiar relationship with Homer and that was enough. Her excitement about the party ebbed away quickly, since the level it had reached on the flat beach of her consciousness had been only relatively high; she sank back into stagnancy and the room was silent against the jangling cries of the hillbilly band which had replaced the Purina man at his insistence.

"Hev yuh evah bin bahlooHOO," the radio mournfully sang, "Hev yuh evah bin loHONEly, hev yuh evah bin bahloo . . ."

"Say!" said Homer's male friend, and in a falsetto, sad and thin, he whined, "Aw haw!" and snapped his fingers in admiration, nodding at the radio. Homer glared at him.

"I'n play that," he said. "Come on," and he walked out of the room into the hall, followed by the other boy and, without having spoken a word, the two girls. They went down the hall and entered the bedroom Homer shared with his brothers. The door closed behind them and in a moment Mrs. Fisher and Weldon heard the twang of Homer's guitar and the angry whine of his voice.

"Hev yuh evah bin loHONEly, hev yuh evah bin bahloo-HOO," he sang, sounding almost exactly like the man on the radio, striving, it seemed, for the coyote's piercing wail of longing and lone, barren desire.

Mrs. Fisher and Weldon sat in the front room, unmoving, as stolid and controlled as a pair of Al Capones, their eyes calm, almost lifeless. Mrs. Fisher felt the situation had altered and probably in the wrong direction, if it had any good or bad characteristics at all, but she was uncertain about it. Drugged with inertia, she allowed the fact, "they in the bedroom," to appear before her without any sentiment attached to it whatever. Weldon's thoughts were more active. He wondered what they were doing in there. They listened to Homer's voice and the primitive guitar for several minutes, and then the sounds stopped.

"Every penny counts nowadays," the man on the radio said.

"Increase the output of your hens with Purina egg mash. Don't delay, do it today, with the red and white checkered Purina."

The hillbilly band started again and a thin, cowpuncher voice sang of the Alamo and a Comanche maiden in the moonlight.

"He'll kill him," Mrs. Fisher said. "That's what he'll do, he'll just kill him."

"What?" Raymond stood in the doorway with a saucer of ice cream and cake in each hand. "What is it, Mama?"

Mrs. Fisher did not look at him.

"Where they got to now?" said Raymond, standing there with the saucers. "Here I done dished up the party stuff and they ain't here."

He sat down next to his mother and looked from her to Weldon. His brother, still holding his position of outraged dignity, turned his head toward him.

"They in the bedroom," he said.

"The bedroom?" Raymond sounded disgusted. "What for? They can't hear no radio in there," and he put the saucers down on the floor. "What you sittin' there so funny for?" he asked his brother. "What the matter with you, anyway?"

"Hush up, now," said Mrs. Fisher, and she rose from the sofa and shuffled down the hall to the bedroom door, facing it, bent forward slightly.

"Homer!" she cried. "I know you in there!"

There was no sound from the bedroom.

"I'll get a stick!" Mrs. Fisher said, but she did not try to open the door. She waited a moment, then called. "The ice cream's meltin'."

"Lemme take 'em a saucer," Raymond said. He stood at her side, looking up at her with a happy smile, proud of the ice cream and cake, eager to make friends with Homer's guests.

"Git!" said Mrs. Fisher, and she slapped him.

Raymond stood there for a moment, eight years old, a BYPU member, unable to believe what had happened. Then the sting spread from his face over his body and he was suddenly unbearably ashamed of the day, the house and everybody in it, including himself.

"Wah!" he screamed, running down the hall toward the back porch. "I never done nothing!" and as he rushed for the screen door he met his father, coming in.

Mr. Fisher was not a good salesman; the light did not burn within him and this was a fatal darkness. His heaviness, his lowering offer of his wares was noticed even in the Mexican restaurants, or perhaps especially there, and on the day of Homer's party he had canvassed the Mexican section of town, exhibiting his cement-like pies indifferently, brooding about the Katy railroad until he could stand it no longer. He went home earlier than usual.

When he turned into the driveway and saw the Ford roadster parked there, the whorish, insolent little car in his yard, he knew instantly what had happened and at once began cursing and shouting threats. He jumped from the sedan before it stopped and was on the back porch, thrusting Raymond aside, before the car ran up against the garage and halted with a sound of splintering wood.

"Where is he!" roared Mr. Fisher, rushing up the hall to his wife, undoing his belt as he went. "Where is that drunkard, that whoremonger!"

Mrs. Fisher stood in front of the bedroom door, still holding her slight stooping position. She looked calmly and absolutely unbelievingly at her husband and might have remained there indefinitely if Homer had not jerked the door open and jumped into the hall, wearing nothing but his underwear shorts.

During the blink of an eyelid the trio stood bunched up in front of the open door, then Mr. Fisher's arm rose with the belt and Homer leaped back into the room, slamming the door behind him. Mr. Fisher immediately launched himself against it.

"Now you listen!" Homer cried from the other side. "These here is high-class people, Daddy!"

"Ah!" grunted Mr. Fisher, crashing rhythmically against the door. "Ah! Ah!"

Mrs. Fisher turned and shuffled unhurriedly back to the front room. She pushed Weldon aside as she entered and reseated herself on the sofa. Weldon went back to his chair by the radio and they sat as they had before, but breathing heavily this time.

From the hallway came the steady thudding sounds of Mr. Fisher's body against the door and Homer's muffled shouts from the bedroom, mingled with other, foreign cries, treble wails made by the girls as they dressed themselves and crawled out a window, followed by Homer's boy friend. Mrs. Fisher and Weldon heard the Ford start, backfire, and roar in reverse down the driveway and into the street, but they did not get up to look outside. That part of the day, of life, was finished; it held no interest for them any longer. At the same time the activity at the bedroom door was hardly mysterious; they were not titillated by that, either. They sat on in the front room in vegetable, breathing stillness, waiting.

After his father crashed past him Raymond continued his flight from the house, screaming with outrage and shame. He ran into the shed and clambered wildly about over barrels and boxes, then settled down in a corner behind the broken remains of a rabbit hutch, relic of one of Mr. Fisher's earlier, less frantic attempts at self-sufficiency.

"I never done a single thing!" he said to the boxes and barrels, and tears streamed down his cheeks as he thought of the slap, the entrance of his father and the abrupt disintegration of Homer's party or what had been intended as Homer's party since for Raymond it had never begun. The sponge white cake in its neat cardboard package, and the green ice cream! All lost now, scattered and smashed like all dreams of good things.

"I'm on show him some day," muttered Raymond, clenching his fists. "He ain't even a Christian daddy at all," and he imagined the triumph of love and God, the gentle, childish triumvirate of Father, Son and Holy Ghost ruling in this house, washing all sins away.

If only I done turned the other cheek, he thought, if only I remembered to do that. Next time I will, and he felt better, a soft, forgiving smile parted his wet lips and he squatted farther down behind the rabbit hutch, waiting for Homer's punishment to begin and then end, while in the house Mr. Fisher, in the agony of 1932, crashed rhythmically against the bedroom door.

mavis at the beach

⚋ I inherited Mavis, really. She used to be the girl friend of the fellow who owned the house I rented on ramshackle Perry Lane back of the Stanford campus beyond the golf course. There aren't many crackpots at Stanford, but they all live on Perry Lane.

Mavis' father was a famous psychologist and he had raised her on strict laboratory principles, but that hadn't worked, and she had a job as a curbhop at a drive-in restaurant on El Camino Real. Every morning at three o'clock she'd walk to Perry Lane, carrying a bowl of Rice Krispies and a pint of milk, and go into the house and squat down by the bed and pour the milk over the Rice Krispies, to wake up the fellow who owned the house. This got on his nerves after a while, and he bought a goat named Sebastian and tethered him in the front yard, because Mavis was afraid of goats, but she still managed to get into the house every morning and squat down by his bed, so he rented the house to me and went away. The second morning I lived there Mavis squatted down by my bed and I awoke to the crackling sound of breakfast food, and that started it. As for Sebastian the goat, he had no luck at all.

I awoke one morning and found, when I looked warily into the front yard for what the night had left, that Sebastian was hanging from the oak, suspended by his collar and chain from an upper limb, with his hind legs about three feet from the scrubby grass. He was dead, hanged in his sassy attempt to climb to greener leaves, apparently, cocky enough to make it to the first horizontal limb, but not thoughtful enough to remember the chain. Perhaps he had leaped down for the ground, only to be brought up short by his tether; perhaps he had slipped; I never knew.

I unhooked Sebastian from his collar and pulled the chain out of the oak and took him to the Palo Alto dump in the pickup, down respectable University Avenue and a bumpy road out near the yacht basin, and laid him in the dump, next to a pile of charred palm-tree stumps the city had left there. When I got back to Perry Lane, Mavis was sitting on the front yard chewing on a twig. I went into my house and pretty soon Mavis followed me and made us cups of instant coffee. She was wearing jeans and a big, faded grey sweat shirt with ATHLETIC DEPT. stenciled across the back, and you could tell, as you could always tell about Mavis, that she was naked underneath; what you saw Mavis was wearing was all Mavis was wearing. Dear Mavis. With instant coffee, she was all I needed to start the day.

"The goat is gone," she said, and sipped her coffee. She was sitting on the floor, of course, since she never sat on anything except floors, earth, motorcar seats and beds, and I was sitting in a four-dollar rattan chair that was standard equipment on Perry Lane, looking down at her and creaking thoughtfully from time to time, waking up, with the faint smell of goat hair on my hands.

"Yes," I said. "You won't have to worry about Sebastian any more. Just you and me and Nescafé. It's kind of a caffeine paradise, when you stop and think about it. Ha, ha," I said, and crossed my legs sort of savagely, thinking, it's only nine in the morning, for God's sake.

A car drove up outside and a horn honked. I looked out the

window and it was George, in his old Plymouth station wagon, with Sally in the front seat beside him, and Jacques, their twelve-year-old son, in the seat behind. Sticking up behind Jacques was the end of a loaf of French bread and a little clump of bottle necks. A picnic. I walked over to the door and looked out, and Sally saw me. I shut the door and went back to my chair and sank creaking into it, while Mavis watched with half-shut eyes, a cigarette dangling from her unpainted mouth.

From out in the yard came the scratching, tormented sound of somebody playing the scales on a violin. That was Jacques, of course; George encouraged the boy in the notion that he was, instinctively, with no training whatever, musical. Or he did at that period, anyway. At another time when I knew them Jacques was whining for a pet like all the other children and George got him a sponge from the hardware store, not even a genuine sponge but a plastic one, some profitable by-product of the Du Ponts, and Jacques put it in a goldfish bowl of water and fed it fish food every night. It made a wonderfully quiet pet, that sponge, and there was very little mess connected with it, just a few flakes of fish food spilled on the floor occasionally.

But at this time of Sebastian and Mavis, Jacques was in his musical phase, or George was, and I sat in silence with Mavis, listening to those dreadful noises, while George kept honking the horn, and while all that was going on my front door opened and Sally came in.

She said hello, standing in the doorway, and I said hello, and then she saw Mavis sitting on the floor looking up at her and she said, very formally, that she was sorry she and George hadn't seen more of me and they certainly hoped they would, and Hello, Mavis, how are you? Mavis smiled and didn't say anything. She slid her hand under her sweat shirt (it was her sweat shirt now, anyway), and scratched her stomach, watching Sally. Don't ask why, but it was a pretty insulting maneuver, and I got up and asked Sally if she wanted a cup of coffee. She said, Oh, no, thank you, that would be too much trouble and I said, Nonsense, it was no trouble at all, after all it was just instant coffee, ha, ha, but she said No, really, they were on their way to a picnic at the beach, they'd just stopped by for a minute to see if, ah, we wouldn't all like to go along, and Mavis got up off the floor.

"Oh, balls," she said. "Me Tondelayo. Me make you tiffin," and she padded off to the kitchen, her tight round bottom switching insolently as she went.

"She just dropped by or something," I said. "She heard about Sebastian and she just sort of came by to check up, I guess. How are you? Are you all right?"

Sally looked at me and frowned slightly. "I'd heard she was living here," she said. "I'm fine, of course. How are you?"

"Oh, no," I said. "She's not living here at all. Where'd you hear anything like that?"

"What's wrong with a little sex?" Sally said. "That's what Perry Lane is for, isn't it? Where'd she get that Tondelayo stuff?"

"She must've seen that old Gable-Hedy Lamarr picture," I said. "You know, over at the Union. They have old movies over there every Sunday, I think."

"You mean you must've seen it," Sally said, and Mavis came back with a plastic bathroom cup full of coffee. She handed it to Sally and sat on the floor again, scratching higher up this time under the sweat shirt.

"Come on," Sally said, "let's all go to the beach."

We went out and Mavis got in the back seat with Jacques and his fiddle and I sat up front next to Sally, with George on the other side of her, clutching the wheel, and we drove off, rather furiously, Jacques trying desperately to play the scales as he lurched back and forth against Mavis, his bow poking us in the neck as he sawed away.

"That's lovely," I heard Mavis murmur to him. "Attaboy."

George took the back road out of the campus, across those

rolling meadows the color of an old lion lying in the sun and up to
the crest of the coast range. At Sky Londa we turned left and
started down the other side, through the redwoods, dark, mossy,
green and damp, a narrow, broken asphalt road like the kind that
always leads to a Girl Scouts' camp. There was a lot of road
construction going on around La Honda and the detours were so
bumpy that Jacques quit trying the scales and said he had to go to
the bathroom. George stopped at a bar and told Jacques to go on,
and then he got out and went in, too. I said we might as well all
go in, and we did, and George was standing at the bar with an
empty shot glass in front of him, drinking ginger ale from a
bottle.

"I've been feeling kind of tense, all morning," he told Sally, but
she didn't look at him. She sat on a bar stool and ordered a glass of
white wine and so did I, and Mavis walked barefoot over to the
jukebox and squatted in front of it, reading the titles or watching
the colored lights, God knows which. We heard a toilet flush
someplace and Jacques came into the barroom from the back,
carrying his fiddle in one hand and his bow in the other, with his
fly undone. George yelled at him to zip himself up, but he was
wearing blue jeans with buttons and he couldn't manage it
because of the fiddle and bow, which he obviously didn't want to
let out of his hands, and George finally ran over to him and got
the bow away from him after a while, with both of them yelling
and shouting, while Sally sat at the bar, looking at herself in the
mirror and drinking her California Chablis. The wine was so cold
you could hardly taste it and I ordered two more.

Jacques buttoned himself up with one hand at last, watching
his father with his big, round, expressionless face while he did it,
like a Western movie star staring at his opponent while he buckles
on his gun belt, and George stood over him with the bow,
watching and mumbling, until the job was finally done and they
came over to the bar. George ordered a straight brandy and
Jacques told his mother he wanted a chocolate milk, which they

didn't have. George handed him the almost half-empty bottle of ginger ale and told him to shut up, and Jacques told his father to give him back his fiddle bow.

"Or else I won't go on your old picnic," he said, leaning against Sally.

"Oh, Christ," George said. He ordered another brandy, drank it right down, and slid the bow down the bar where Jacques could pick it up. "I don't know," George said. "I really don't." He sounded tired, instead of tense. It occurred to me that in a year or so Jacques would weigh more than George, and I felt sorry for George.

"This is a half-assed kind of picnic, isn't it?" Mavis said. She had lost interest in the jukebox and she leaned against me, looking at Jacques, who was still leaning against Sally. Jacques looked back at Mavis with that noncommittal face of his, his mouth open in a little fat O, the ginger-ale bottle suspended halfway between the bar and his lips.

"Where'd you get that atha-letic shirt?" he asked Mavis.

"From a jock strap," she said, and Sally shoved Jacques with her elbow.

"Go on outside and play or something," she told him, but he didn't. He looked from Sally to Mavis, and then kept on looking at Mavis. "I wanta atha-letic shirt like that," he said.

"All right," Sally said. "Later. But go on outside."

"I want that atha-letic shirt," Jacques said.

"Come and get it," Mavis told him, leaning harder against me. "I dare you. What are you, yellow?" But Sally got down from her stool and herded George from his.

"Come on," she said. "Let's get on to the beach, for God's sake."

"This is the kind of picnic I like," Mavis said as we filed out and climbed into the car. "A gloomy picnic. Maybe it'll rain."

"No," George said. "It never rains at the beach. Not at this time of the year. That's one of the peculiarities of the Peninsula. In the summer it—"

"Look out for that bulldozer, for Christ's sake," Sally said. "They're ruining this whole area, just ruining it. Look at that. They're knocking over hundreds of trees."

"What'll you take for that atha-letic shirt," Jacques said.

"I'll tell you later," Mavis said. "Go on and play with your toy. The fiddle, I mean." And George drove a little faster through the redwoods, while the dreadful seesaw sounds of horsehair on gut screeched at our backs and Mavis rested one bare foot on the seat behind my head and tickled my neck with her toes. After a while Sally made Jacques pass the picnic basket up front and we shared swigs from a bottle of red, because she said George needed both hands to drive. It struck me that I hadn't read a newspaper in months, and I unwrapped the one Sally had folded around a bottle to keep it from breaking and tried to read it, but the effort was too much on that road at that speed, and I finally stuffed it back in the basket because Sally said we might need a paper to start a fire.

At San Gregorio beach you park the car on a kind of headland and creep down to the sand, then walk through the shallow water of a creek which always has artichokes floating in it from the farms upstream, their leaves browned at the tips, bobbing along to the Pacific, each worth about fifteen cents in the Midwest. I don't know why they're in that creek; I used to ask Californians about it, but they always gave me vague, unsatisfactory answers. George said they were culls, but culls from what? And why were they put into the creek? He didn't know, but he always mumbled something about the Mexican pickers and I think he believed this was a kind of sabotage practiced by the pickers against the gringo farmers, and I also think in his own mind he referred to the farmers as "absentee landlords," a holdover from his days as Diego Rivera's assistant on the San Francisco murals.

We parked the car on the headland and everybody got out. There was only one other car there, a Pontiac convertible with nobody in it, but George was annoyed, because he wanted the beach all to himself, I guess. He frowned at the Pontiac.

"Damned tourists," he said. The Pontiac had California plates and Mavis walked over and pointed at the plate on the rear, grinning at George, but he ignored her. Jacques must've thought it was some new kind of a game, because he went over and pointed at the plate, too, looking at his father but not grinning at all.

"Oh, God damn it," George said, "let's go." And he disappeared over the edge of the headland, waving his arms to keep his balance. There was a cold wind blowing from the sea, and the sky was overcast. By the time we all got down to the beach a light rain had started and we stood around in it at the foot of the headland, arguing about how long it would probably last. George said it would be over in a few minutes, but Sally said she didn't want to stand there until it quit. Jacques and Mavis thought we ought to find a cave, but George said the tide was in and all the caves would be full of water. I didn't know whether the tide was in or out, but Jacques said it wasn't, either, in, and Mavis said it didn't make any difference, we could all take off our clothes and have a nude picnic in the cave. That shut Jacques up, all right, although he kept staring at Mavis, but Sally said there wouldn't be any place to hang our clothes in a cave so we all trooped back up the cliffside and got in the station wagon. The Pontiac was gone.

"I think the kid has to go to the can," Mavis said. Jacques was squirming around and sort of clawing at his crotch, but he said he didn't, either, have to go.

"It's his trunks," Sally said. "He's got on his bathing trunks under his jeans."

"Well, take 'em off," Mavis said.

"Go back to that gas station," Sally told George. "He can change in the men's room."

"All right," George said. "I think they have a bar, too. We can wait out this rain there."

The Pontiac was parked in the station driveway. I didn't believe the place had a bar, but it did, or anyway a liquor license. You sat in the office, a room about ten feet square, with cans of oil stacked along the walls, cards of fan belts dangling from the rafters and a metal stand with a white-walled tire on it in the middle of everything, and the owner made drinks on his desk. He kept the bottles on a shelf in a clump of lighter fluid and Never-Leak cans, and when we walked in he was pouring two brandies for the people from the Pontiac.

"Well," George said. "For heaven's sake." And he shook hands with a blonde girl and a young man with a golden beard, while Sally said, Hello, how do you do, and Mavis just grinned. Jacques went to the men's room, and I was introduced to Joan and the Jesus character, whose name I never heard.

"You folks know each other, do you?" said the gas-station man. He was about sixty-five, tanned and stringy, in a suit of spotless, starched khakis. His voice was sort of professionally hoarse, as though he had spent his life talking against the wind or some other annoying noise, and he spoke out of the corner of his mouth like those men who sell dancing dolls on the sidewalks around Times Square. "Well, now, ain't that fine," he said, smiling at everybody. "Make yourselves at home. Have your picnic in here if you want." He nodded at our picnic basket. "Except for liquor, of course. Can't let you bring your own liquor in. Against the law, believe it or not. Ha, ha."

"It's not liquor," George said. "It's just wine. But give us all a brandy, anyway. Well," he said to Joan. "Well. How are you?"

"Wine is still liquor," the gas man said. "According to the law. Can't do that."

"I'm all right," she said. "In fact, I suppose I'm fine. How are you? Have you recovered? Are you returned to normalcy?"

"What?"

"You know. Since you spent the night at my place."

"Have I missed something?" Sally said.

"I thought you probably knew about it," Joan told her. "It was kind of funny, in a way. I don't think George knew where he was."

"An elevator shaft?" I asked her. "Do you live in a kind of an elevator shaft?"

She looked at me.

"Who are you?" she said. "Are you that new friend of Mavis'? I've heard about you." She looked at Mavis and smiled, and Mavis smiled back. They seemed to like each other, which seemed odd.

"An elevator shaft," Sally said. "Just what is all this about an elevator shaft?"

"I guess you haven't seen it," Joan said. "My new apartment. Everybody says it reminds them of an elevator shaft."

"Oh, yes," Sally said.

"Very Freudian," said the bearded young man.

"Balls," Mavis said, but nobody paid attention except the gas-station man.

"I think I told you about it," George said. "Let's have another brandy," he told the gas man, looking nervously around the room, which was certainly much too small for this sort of thing, even in my opinion, and I wasn't there with my wife.

"No," Sally said. "I don't think you did."

"It was the mosaic design for that damned lawyer's bathroom," George said. "I told you about it. I know I did. I went up there to see him about, ah, about it, and—"

"Oh, God," Sally said, and sighed. "You're too old for that nonsense, George, don't you know that? Ever since you had your gall bladder out the doctor said—"

"God damn it, I know that," George said. "That's not the way it was at all."

"No wonder you didn't get the commission," Sally said. "I don't blame the man now, after hearing what an ass you must've made of yourself."

"No," George said. "That isn't it at all. I didn't even see him that night. It was the next day."

"What kind of a picnic is this?" Mavis said. "Why don't you

knock off all that crap. You can do this at home, on your own time, for Christ's sake."

"Good point," the bearded young man said.

"Have your picnic in here if you want," the gas man said. "Except for the liquor. Can't let you bring your own liquor in with you. Against the law. But make yourselves at home."

"Oh, don't be so damn middle-class," Sally said to everybody. She picked up a glass of brandy and looked around for an exit, but there wasn't any, except the door leading to the grease rack and the men's room, so she sat down on a battery on the window ledge and ignored us.

"You'll get acid," George told her. "You're sitting on a battery." But she didn't answer and the gas man said, No, there wasn't any acid, it was a new battery and it didn't even have any water in it yet, and we heard a toilet flushing someplace and Jacques came in. He was wearing tight maroon lastex swimming trunks like a pantie girdle and high-topped GI shoes and nothing else, and his belly bulged over the lastex trunks and the tops of the shoes cut into his fat ankles and he was playing the scale on the fiddle, staring at George.

"My God," Mavis said. "This is the worst picnic I ever saw."

"Where the hell did he leave his pants?" George shouted to Sally. "I mean why did he leave his pants? Why did you leave your pants?" he yelled at Jacques, but the boy just kept staring at him, sawing away on the fiddle.

"Good heavens," the bearded young man said.

"Go right ahead," the gas man said. "Just go right ahead and have your picnic in here. He's a hefty little chap, ain't he?"

"By God," George yelled, "if you can't learn to control him better than that you never should've had a child in the first place! By God, you just can't function as a mother, why don't you admit it!" And Sally hooked her finger at him in a rude gesture, and Jacques kept sawing away and Mavis started scratching her stomach under her waistband and the gas man nodded and smiled at Jacques.

"Well," he said. "Learning to play, are you? That's fine. I had me a jew's-harp when I was your age." He held his hands up to his mouth and flapped them around, but George dragged Jacques out the door into the grease-rack room and the fiddle died horribly. A door slammed, and we could hear George's voice, far off but full, and Jacques' thin and distant, arguing in the men's room.

"Would you get me another brandy, please," Sally said, still sitting on the battery, and I told the gas man to give us all one. "I really do think it's going to rain all day, I really do," she said, staring out the streaked plate glass.

"I told you we should've gone to the cave," Mavis said, and sat down on the floor. "At least we could've stripped there. It's hot in here."

"Going swimming, were you?" the gas man said, pouring brandies. "Well, we get a lot of that, around here. Don't care for it, myself. Of course, it's all in what you're used to. I've seen the whole country, one time or another, but I never could get to like the water. Never did."

"Is that so," Joan said. "Done a lot of traveling? Not a native Californian?"

"Oh, no, no," the gas man said. "Started out in Ohio. Ran away from home when I was thirteen and joined the circus. Wanted to be a pony boy. Back around 1903, that was. Ha! Pony boy! Too damned much work in that, I'll tell you. No, no, I didn't go for that. None of that pony boy stuff for *me*. Soon as I got squared away I seen what I wanted to be was a talker, what you folks call a barker. Standing up there talking the people in. I just like to see folks entertained, I guess, always did."

"Oh," Joan said. "You were a barker? A talker? A carnival man?"

"Freaks," the gas man said. "Managed world's biggest midway freak and side show for twenty-eight years. Gave the people entertainment, did a great thing for the freaks, made a good, comfortable living, good life, no matter how you look at it."

"Good heavens," the bearded young man said.

"Oh, yes," the gas man said. "I sold Maida Tully, the little girl without any extremities whatsoever, to Ripley in 1932. You remember her, of course; people still talk about her. Found her on a farm down near Alta, Georgia. Ten years old at the time. Parents were undesirables, of course. Had child labor laws in those days, too, you know, but with no extremities of any kind it was hard to tell just how old she was. My wife took her in and got her a permanent wave and you'd never have known her age. Worked wonders. Taught her everything she knew, my wife did. Parents were absolutely undesirable. Used to come around every time the show played a still date at Atlanta and cry when they saw Maida Tully on the stage. But it was the money, that's what they wanted, the money. After the money started rolling in you couldn't tell *those* folks I wasn't the greatest thing on God's green earth, and show business, too. Of course you remember the elephant boy, had this long growth, you might say deformity, hung down from one ear, we called him the elephant boy, I bought him in Milledgeville, Georgia, parents were absolutely undesirable, a lot of whoring and drinking in the family, but his grandparents were wonderful people. Well, I got a judge down there to make me his guardian, and his grandparents—they didn't have no electricity, lived in a shack with shutters instead of windows—why, nothing would do but they had to have an electric washer. One of the first models ever made, hauled it out there and set it up on their porch. They were the happiest old couple you ever saw, just thought the world and all of me."

George came in with Jacques, who was now wearing his trousers and carrying the fiddle. George had the bow and he waved it at the gas man when he came in.

"I think I'll have a brandy," he said. "I've been feeling kind of tense all day."

"I was just telling the folks," the gas man said, pouring the brandy, "you never know what people are going to like. I remember once a fellow came up to me in Murfree, Alabama, told me he had a child with a fifty-five-pound head and a fifteen-pound body, child never had developed normally, just the head, and I said, No, no, I told myself, the public won't go for that, they'll think it's a deformity, but you know, I've never been so surprised in my life, that child was a sensation, everywhere we went. One of the most successful freaks I ever had. You just never can tell what the public will go for."

"What?" George said.

"Freaks," the gas man said. "Did them a world of good, and of course did all right for yourself, too. Showed the world they were good for something, could make their own way. We had one boy with no extremities whatsoever and he painted beautiful, artistic pictures. Held the brush in his mouth. You found most of them in little towns down South in those days. I'd keep a little black book, you know, and whenever I'd hear of a good, interesting freak, I'd make a note on it and try and get back around that way. Of course, it had to be a good, interesting freak, not some deformity, you might say. We had to sell these freaks, don't forget, and you can't sell deformity, not as a rule. Public just won't go for it somehow."

"What?"

"Oh, I could tell you I don't know how many interesting things happened. We had a very pleasant thing just before I left the show. One of our freaks, young fellow with two perfectly formed faces, had two mouths, two noses and a third eye in the center of his forehead, a very peculiar character, why, he decides he's in love with one of the girl freaks—had alligator skin if you know what that is—skin an inch thick over her entire body. Be damned if they didn't get married. We gave them a house trailer and a real good sendoff and they went back to his folks' place, a farm in Mississippi. Of course, the business is dead now. Everybody has too much money. They have a freak and right away something's done for it, the doctors take it or it's put away someplace where nobody can see it or get at it. Just ruined the business. That's why I got out. It wasn't TV hurt the business at all. But it was a good business for me. I'll say that. A lot of interesting times, you know."

"You dirty son of a bitch," Mavis said.

"Ha, ha," the gas man said. "Well, now, Miss, I guess it might seem that way to somebody not in the business, but you just take it from me—"

"You horrible son of a bitch," Mavis said, and she stood up and threw a quart can of motor oil at him. The can struck the gas man's forehead with a heavy, solid thud and fell lumpishly to the floor, *thwack!* and rolled a little. The gas man fell face down on his desk and his skin began to turn grey-blue.

"Mama," Jacques said, "she used a nasty word." But George slapped him and then threw his arms around Mavis, but she was just standing there, looking calmly at the gas-station man.

"Get the oil can," Joan said, and I did, and carried it out to the station wagon and put it on the floor, and then I went back and got the picnic basket and Sally. I started to go back for Mavis and George and Jacques, but they were already on their way out. Joan and the bearded young man got in the Pontiac with Joan behind the wheel, and she called to me that they'd see us in San Francisco at her place, and they drove off, and then we drove off in the rain. They took the coast road north and we went back over the mountains toward 101, and nobody said anything until we got to the top of the coast range and started down toward the bay. The sun was shining on the Peninsula, and there were boats in the bay, and the yellow and red dots that were MG's crawled along Sand Hill road. I turned around and looked back at Mavis. Jacques was asleep on her shoulder and she grinned at me.

"I'll bet they don't have picnics like this back in the East, do they?" she said.

my escape
from the cia

❖   Since the Central Intelligence Agency is in so much hot
water anyway because of its role in such international blunders as
the U-2 incident and the invasion fiasco in Cuba, not to mention
that fellow they tried to bribe in Singapore, I think it's time I
made a clean breast of my own connection with the organization,
not only to get the whole thing off my conscience, but also to
permit the CIA to close its file on me. The last time I heard from
them, they still had my file open, and they may be waiting for me
to show up in Washington and go to work. The way things are
going for them now, I imagine they'd like to get all such
unfinished business cleared up so the files can be carted off for
storage in a government warehouse someplace.

I would never have had anything to do with the CIA at all if I
had not found myself in California in 1952, enrolled in a large
university on the GI bill at the age of thirty, stone broke and in
the middle of a divorce. The only clothing I owned was four pairs
of khakis, three sweat shirts, a tweed jacket with leather elbow
patches which had been put on by the former owner, one pair of
low-quarter sneakers, one pair of run-over moccasins, and several
shirts and shorts which I had bought in a Junior League Thrift

Shop. Transportation is vital in California, but all I had was a Chevrolet pickup truck which I had wrecked twice while the divorce was still in the early stages. By American standards—and God knows by California standards—I was thoroughly unemployable, and it was then that the CIA entered my life.

At first I didn't know it was the CIA. An English professor who had befriended me (largely, I think, because of those elbow patches: you don't see many of those in California, and he was a Harvard man) invited me to a cocktail party at his house, and since I had borrowed five hundred dollars from him to pay a very complicated traffic fine, I was eager to please, and so I went to the party. Actually, I probably would have gone even if I hadn't borrowed the five hundred dollars, because I liked him and because I couldn't afford to turn down an evening of free drinks.

Anyway, I showed up, and before I'd finished the first free drink the host came up and drew me aside, as they say.

"There's somebody here I want you to meet," he said, looking around.

This struck me as a pretty silly thing to say at a cocktail party, but there was that five hundred bucks to think about, so I smiled, and looked around at all the people, ready to meet somebody. "There he is," the host said. "You go on in the bedroom and I'll bring him in after a minute."

"In the bedroom? Why do we have to meet in the bedroom?"

"You can talk better in there," the host said, and pushed me toward the hall. I went into the bedroom and sat down on the bed, thinking back over the years' poor judgments and small disasters which had led me there, and after a while the host came in with a man and introduced him.

"I'm sure you two will get along fine," my friend said, and winked at me before he left, closing the door behind me.

"Well!" said the newcomer. "Let's get comfortable, shall we?" and we both sat down on the bed. He was about thirty-five years old, six feet or six feet one, a handsome fellow with a rugged, tan face, very genial looking, with an absolutely winning smile. He was dressed well but quietly, and it was pretty obvious he'd never had on somebody else's tweed jacket in his life.

"Tell me about yourself," he said, holding the winning smile.

Now, if someone should ask me to tell him about myself today, I'd probably refuse to do it, but at the time I remember feeling flattered that anybody cared enough to ask, and I expect I must have sensed money somewhere, but anyway, I did tell him about myself, for about thirty minutes. Any personnel manager in his right mind, if given that half-hour's blabber in a résumé, could draw only one conclusion: unstable and probably *permanently* unemployable. But my new friend just nodded and kept smiling while I told him of all the jobs I'd had, from Texas to Minnesota and back again, working as a newspaper reporter, a door-to-door photographer of children, and, for one marvelous week, as a hot-dog-stand counterman in a city zoo. I think I even told him about the five-hundred-dollar traffic conviction, and I know I told him about the divorce. When I got through, the first thing he said was, "You've never been convicted of any Federal charges, have you?" and after giving it a little thought, I said I hadn't.

"Well," he said, getting up. "I think I might have something that might interest you. Today is Monday. Wednesday afternoon, I'll drop by your place and we'll chat some more, around four o'clock. Where do you live?"

I lived in a dormitory with about two thousand noisy under-graduates, and I told him so.

"Fine," he said. "See you Wednesday, then," and we went back to the party. The rest of the evening was pretty uneventful, except for a lady novelist who got too much to drink, but my bedroom acquaintance left the party long before that happened.

I had no real notion of what the man might have that would "interest me"; I suppose I must have expected a sort of public-relations job, since public-relations jobs have always sounded just about as vague as he did. I was in my cell-like room at four o'clock on Wednesday, ready to go to work, wearing a freshly purchased Brooks Brothers shirt from the Junior League Thrift Shop . . . but it wasn't that easy, of course.

When my man arrived, he was wearing casual sports clothes and carrying a large brief case. We sat down on the narrow bed, since there were no chairs in the room, and he picked the brief case up and held it on his lap.

"You do understand, don't you, that I'm with the Government?" he said, smiling. I think maybe he even chuckled.

"No," I said.

"Oh, well," he said. "I guess we'd better start at the beginning, hadn't we?"

"Yes," I said, "certainly," but I had an uneasy thought that the whole thing was going to turn out to have something to do with the census.

"You've heard of the CIA, I imagine?" he said, and now instead of that winning smile he was all seriousness, man-to-man, a Jack Armstrong sort of look, Jack Armstrong prepared to let a friend in on a little secret. I said yes, I had heard of the CIA, and he said he was the West Coast recruiting officer for the boys in Washington, and my professor friend had suggested my name as a possible candidate for employment with the outfit.

Well! I was delighted. Visions of expensive trench coats danced through my head, but since I'm as familiar with espionage thrillers as the next man, I kept a straight face. "I see," I said, patting my pockets for cigarettes. He offered me one from a silver case which had his name engraved on it, and I was mildly disappointed to see it was the same name he was using with me.

"Why is the, uh, outfit interested in me?" I wanted to know. "Because I've had sort of a knock-about life? I mean, running around the country, doing different things? I suppose it's sort of hard to find people who—"

"No," he said, "it's your newspaper experience we're after. Frankly, your job would be to write reports from, well, from certain countries in Western Europe. But before we get into the details, I'd like you to translate this for me, please," and he whipped out a single sheet of mimeograph paper from the brief case and handed it to me. The sheet was printed in French.

"You mean now? Read it now?"

"Don't read it," he said. "Translate it. As quickly as you can, please."

I stumbled through the thing, discovering as I went along that it was a story taken from a French newspaper about some sort of tribal conflict in Senegal. The phrase, *"chambre des communes,"* or something similar, kept reappearing, and I translated it as "common room" about six times, before realizing it must mean "house of commons." Other than that, I did pretty well, and my visitor said he was pleased.

"A little rusty," he said, smiling again, "but I'm sure you could brush up in a hurry."

I agreed that brushing up would be no trouble at all.

"You understand, of course," he went on, after smiling appreciatively at my enthusiasm, "that this is only the *preliminary* language test. For the particular area where you'd be working, that is. Do you have any Flemish?"

No, I said, I had no Flemish at all, expecting to see that smile die, but it didn't.

"As a matter of fact, very few people have," he said. "I'm sure that won't matter."

"Good," I said. "Fine."

He explained there would be another language test given at a certain address in San Francisco on Monday; we shook hands and he left.

I can't remember exactly how I spent those intervening days, but I'm sure they were among the happiest, most exciting I've ever known. I looked at the world through brand-new eyes, eyes that had a tendency to narrow to slits for no reason at all; I found myself memorizing license plates on cars ahead of me in traffic, and eavesdropping unmercifully in the college coffee joint. The high point came on Saturday, when I discovered a Burberry trench coat at the Junior League Thrift Shop, so old and faded it was like white muslin, but the genuine British article, for five dollars. I didn't own a slouch hat, but I had a tweed cap I had stolen from Allen Tate when I was a student of his at the University of Minnesota, and I wore that with the Burberry as I tooled around under the California sunshine in my battered pickup truck, keeping one eye on those suspicious license numbers ahead of me and the other on the rearview mirror, in case I was being followed. And the odd thing was, I *was* being followed: several times that Saturday I spotted a 1948 green Pontiac sedan on my tail, and when I left the Heidelberg Beer Garden at two o'clock Sunday morning, it was parked across the street in a Frostee Malt drive-in. I zoomed off around the first corner and didn't see it again, but I don't think it was just my imagination. As for the truth, of course, it's locked in those files in Washington.

On Monday I drove to San Francisco to the address I had been given (it was a small office building south of Market Street), and presented myself at room number so-and-so. The only occupant was my old friend, but he was all business now, and he promptly put me to work at a table, writing translations of more French newspaper articles. I remember the headline on one of them: it said, *"Télescopage à Dijon!"* and was about two trains which had collided, *malheureusement.*

After about two hours of that, my friend gave me some long forms to fill out, listing all the jobs I'd ever held, where I'd held them, and why I'd quit holding them, as well as a complete record of my educational experiences, going all the way back to my first-grade teacher's name. I couldn't remember my first-grade teacher's name, but I remembered my second-grade teacher's name: Miss Harrison. The reason I could remember it was she had once cast me as a turkey in a play about the Pilgrim Fathers, over my screaming protests, and that's just not the kind of thing a man forgets. So I put her name down, hoping the boys in Washington would consider a second-grade teacher almost as good as a first-grade teacher when it came to giving character references. By the time I got through with all this it was about five o'clock, and the recruiting officer said he was afraid he'd have to be off. I was hoping he'd ask me to have a drink with him in some elegant spot like the Garden Court of the Palace Hotel, where espionage was certain to flourish if it ever flourished anywhere, but he didn't, so I drove on back to the dormitory. In fact, now that I think of it, none of the CIA people I met ever offered to buy me a drink at any time, which is a hell of a way to run a recruiting drive and may have more to do with what happened in Cuba than we suspect.

Several weeks went by before I heard from the boys in Washington again, and when the contact was made, it was on the pay telephone in the hall of the dormitory. I had given that number to the recruiting officer, since I had no telephone of my own, and one day a freshman jerked my door open to say I was wanted on the pay phone. It was the recruiter.

"How does fifty-six hundred a year sound to you?" he said, after we had said hello.

"Fine," I said. "Great." I had about four dollars in cash, sixteen in the bank, and no more than five or six tickets for football games left in my student-activities book.

"Okay, boy," he said, "you'll be hearing from us," and he hung up.

As it turned out, I didn't hear from them for four years, and by that time I was living in a Midwestern city, writing motion-picture scripts for heavy industry, with a new wife, a stepson, a mortgaged ranch-style rambler, and a Ford station wagon. I had long since discarded the Burberry, because I tore a great hole in it getting out of the old pickup truck one day in Sunnyvale, California, where I had gone in search of work in a plant which canned maraschino cherries, but I still had Allen Tate's tweed cap.

This time the contact from the boys in Washington came through the mail. I received a letter without any return address on the envelope informing me that my file had been "reopened" and that I was to arrange as soon as possible to present myself in Washington for an interview. So that there would be no misunderstanding, the letter said, I was to make the trip at my own expense, but in the event of a mutually satisfactory arrangement, I would be reimbursed for travel expenses by the Government. The salary remained the same: fifty-six hundred dollars per year.

I showed the letter to my wife, and then wrote the man in Washington, explaining that my situation was no longer what it had been, that I now had personal responsibilities I had not had before, by which I meant a wife, a child, a mortgage, and a station wagon, and closed by saying, rather proudly, that I was now earning considerably more than the salary offered me and was therefore forced to ask that my file be closed again. I sent this off and forgot about it, but as Mr. Khrushchev knew, the CIA is a persistent crowd. Within two weeks I had another letter from the same fellow in Washington, and this one had a rather nasty tone. It said that the personnel director was at a loss to understand my attitude, that I had stated to a member of the agency that I was willing to accept employment at fifty-six hundred dollars per annum, and that my present demand for a salary almost twice that figure smacked of something pretty unsavory. The letter did not actually threaten me with Federal prosecution, but I am a guilty soul by nature, so instead of simply throwing the letter away, I sat down and wrote a more detailed explanation of my changed condition, closing this time not on a note of pride, but humility: I said I was sorry if I'd caused them any inconvenience, and pointed out that I wasn't asking for any salary at all.

A week later the telephone rang while we were having dinner in our ranch-style rambler, and I answered it.

"My name is Brown," a man's voice said. "I've been asked to

contact you by a friend in Washington." There was a short silence, while I tried to think of some friend in Washington.

"This *is* Hughes Rudd, isn't it?" the voice said, rather impatiently.

"Yes," I said. "But who did you say—"

"It's about that little matter of yours," the voice said. "*You* know. The fifty-six hundred dollars?"

"Oh!" I said. "About that? It's really about that? You called me up about *that*? Where are you? Washington?"

"No, no," the voice said. "I'm here. Write down this address," and he waited while I found a pencil and paper, then read off a street address in a suburb. "Can you make it tomorrow afternoon?" he said. "About four? I'm pretty short on time."

"Well," I said, "I don't get off work until about five."

There was another short, humming silence.

"Oh," he said. "Well, make it five-thirty then. Can you find it? The address, I mean? You know where it is?"

"I'll find it," I said, and added for no reason whatever, "I have a station wagon."

"Okay," the voice said. "And, ah, I probably don't have to tell you—ah, hm. You know what I mean?"

"No," I said. "I couldn't hear you. Tell me what?"

Again the short silence.

"Well, just keep it to yourself," the voice said after a moment, and I could tell it was painful for him to have to come right out and say it.

"Certainly," I said.

Then he mumbled something and hung up.

I wore a new suit to work, since I planned to go straight from the office to the address he'd given me, and I wanted to look my best: I figured I had to *look* like I was making more than fifty-six hundred dollars per annum. The address turned out to be that of a bungalow in an older subdivision which was beginning to go to seed: the front yards of several of the houses had not been mowed in some time, and there were bicycles lying around which had seen heavy use: in my neighborhood everybody mowed his lawn on Saturday, and the bicycles were all new.

I parked the car at the curb and went up to the front door. This lawn was in worse shape than any other on the block, and as I got up to the house, I could see inside because there were no blinds or shades. The rooms were all totally empty of furniture, but all the lights seemed to be on. I knocked on the door, and after a moment I heard somebody come out of the attached garage at one side of the house and clear his throat. I looked around, and a slender man was standing in the driveway in the dusk, looking sort of tired and annoyed.

"Rudd?" he said. "I'm in here," and he went back in the garage.

I followed him inside the garage, he pulled down the overhead door, and we looked at each other in the light cast by a naked bulb in the ceiling. He was about forty-five, wearing glasses on a bony, dispirited nose, and he was dressed in old Air Force fatigues, with a faded Air Force patch on the left shoulder. He didn't offer to shake hands.

"Let's go on inside," he said. "We can talk in there," and we went into the empty house, down some dusty but uncluttered stairs and into the empty basement, where another naked bulb hung from the ceiling. I looked around, but there was no furniture in the basement either, so I remained standing: I didn't feel like sitting on those stairs in my best suit.

"Well," he said, leaning against a wall and lighting a cigarette. "I've been reading your file."

"Oh," I said.

"Yeah," he said. "Who contacted you first?"

"I don't recall his name," I said, right back at him. They might get me for jacking up the price, but not for spilling my guts.

"Okay," he said. "Tell me about yourself."

"Well," I said, "my situation is not what it was, you know. I told them all about myself before. But it's not like that any more. What I mean is, I have a job now."

"What do you mean, 'like it was before'?" he said. "When was that? When you first applied?"

"I didn't apply," I said. "I was, uh, contacted."

"But you don't remember who the contact was," he said, and sneered pretty openly. I opened my mouth, but he held up his hand. "Never mind," he said. "Your application is in your file, and there's a note saying you accepted at fifty-six hundred. Now you want almost twice that. What's that all about, Rudd?"

"That's what I explained," I said. "In the letter. Didn't you—I mean, didn't *they* get my letter? They must've gotten my letter. I explained all that. I owe a lot more money now than I did. I mean, I have a family now."

"Yeah," he said. There was a pause, while he lighted another cigarette. "You know how much I make?" he suddenly asked, glaring at me. "A hell of a lot less than you want. A *hell* of a lot less. And I've been with 'em since 1945."

"Well," I said, but I couldn't think of anything else.

"Okay, Rudd," he said, straightening up from the wall. "I've got to send in a report on this, you understand. I'm pretty pressed for time, but I'll be as fair as I can."

"Well," I said, but he started up the stairs and I followed him back out into the garage. This time I noticed there was an open quart can of cream-colored paint on the floor and a four-inch brush. I looked at them, but I didn't say anything, and I went on out to my car. As I drove away the garage door was still open, and I could see him in there, painting one of the walls with a cigarette dangling from the corner of his mouth, and that was my last contact with the boys in Washington. I never got a letter telling me my case had been closed, and I never wrote to *ask* if it had been closed.

About a year after I saw the man in the empty house I moved away from that city, leaving my ranch-style rambler behind, along with Allen Tate's tweed cap, which somehow or other got thrown out with some old Army pants of mine, and I gradually forgot all about the Central Intelligence Agency until it was accused of ruining Mr. Eisenhower's Summit meeting in Paris. Ever since that happened I've been wondering what had become of my old friend the recruiting officer: he was such a smooth type that I expect he could survive any sort of a bureaucratic shakeup, but I'm not so sure about the garage painter, Mr. Brown. Where in the world, I ask myself, is Mr. Brown? In what garage is he interviewing people now?

no relief in sight

⁂   "I didn't know it was loaded," Mrs. Kozciewski said. "All I meant to do was scare him a little."

"He must have scared pretty hard," Lieutenant Pond said. "How do you spell that last name again?"

Kansas City's summer heat filled the filthy room like a bubble of hot sewer gas. The dirty gauze curtains flapped at the gritty windowsill and a little wind, a breeze it was called, slipped through the room and into the long, stinking hallway. The breeze felt like the air blown onto the dazzling sidewalks by the exhaust fans of cheap restaurants. As the paper said, there was no relief in sight. Tom Moore stood, his pencil in one hand, his folded sheaf of flimsy paper in the other. He could feel sweat drops rolling down his legs, and his shirt collar was soaked. The cloth felt cold against the prickly heat of his neck, and pleasant. He could smell the collar, salty and wet, and he could smell dead coal dust and wet garbage, rotting in the hallway, and the stale smell of greasy clothing, old food odors, unwashed underwear, the mildewed walls and ceilings, hot leather and feet, and Mr. Kozciewski's blood, also hot, and smelling metallic, like streetcar rails in the sun.

Mr. Kozciewski lay across the unmade bed where the shotgun's blast had tossed him, sprawled backward with legs apart and bent, his arms above his head framing the mess where his head had been, framing what looked like a gallon or so of red currant preserves dumped on his shoulders. He was wearing striped seersucker pants and what appeared to be, incredibly, a suit of BVD's. His feet were bare and his toenails, through some trick of reflection or lighting, looked as blue as slate.

"He kept after me and kept after me," Mrs. Kozciewski said. "He just wouldn't leave me alone. And it was so hot."

She was a big, stupid-looking woman in her thirties, wearing a cotton kimono and red plush bedroom slippers. Her hair looked as unmade as the bed, and she kept touching the hair at her temples with her hands.

"Whaddya think they'll do to me," she said. "Ha?"

You could not tell how old Mr. Kozciewski was. The underwear covered his chest where hair might have been gray or black or brown and his arms were white and smooth, long-muscled, of no age, the arms of a workingman. The underwear was made out of some thin material woven in a checked texture and the top of it buttoned down the front with little white buttons, like a garment out of the 1920's.

"How old was your husband, ma'am?" Tom asked, putting the pencil point on the damp paper.

"Why," Mrs. Kozciewski said, turning to him, touching the hair at her temple, "he was forty-three, come to think of it."

Tom wrote it down. Come to think of it, he thought; come to think of it. My God, it was hot! Frank Kozciewski, 43, unemployed.

"He was a restaurant employee, when he could get it," Mrs. Kozciewski said. "You from the paper?"

Unemployed dishwasher, Tom wrote.

"Somebody's got to clean up this mess," Lieutenant Pond said to the patrolman in the doorway. "You got any friends in the building?" he said to the woman. "Anybody who'd like to help you out?"

"Why, I guess so," Mrs. Kozciewski began. She looked from the lieutenant to the man on the bed and stood a moment with her mouth ajar, as though now understanding what the policeman meant.

"Ha!" she said. "Ha! Clean it up yourself! Ha! Ha! Ha!"

"Watch your mouth, lady," Lieutenant Pond said. He turned away from her and stared out the window, his thumbs hooked in his trouser pockets, his hands listless. "Where the hell is that ambulance?" he said. "It's hotter in here than it is on the street."

"I'll see you," Tom said, pocketing his damp sheaf of paper. "I better get back to the office."

"Yeah," Lieutenant Pond said, without turning his head. "Take it easy."

"What do you want to put it in the paper for?" Mrs. Kozciewski said. "What the hell business is it of yours?"

On the sidewalk the sun struck like the steel side of a blazing boxcar, solid and overwhelming. The concrete beneath the soles of his shoes felt gritty and porous, as though the artificial rock were expanding and disintegrating in this bath of white fire. The open doors of saloons made black and solid oblongs in the glare of building fronts, and cooled, beery air spilled out of them, dimming the sun for a moment. But there was no relief there, either. Marjorie was right. That air-conditioned air had cooled too many, too fitfully. After five minutes in the cool, dim bars you began to sweat even more quickly than before, and the icy beer turned lukewarm and sickly in the glass against your palm.

He plodded on through the glittering vacuum, past paint stores, banks, cafés and wholesale hardware houses, past the hellish concentration of heat in parking lots, where the intolerable metal of the cars glared and sizzled, going back to the office. Think of it: no relief in sight!

He stepped from the curb into the street, his soles sinking into the soft, glutinous asphalt, asphalt almost ready to melt and run like syrup, held in place now by surface tension. The asphalt stretched blue and black beneath the thin gray powder of its surface tension, as though someone had dusted the street with talcum, as though a soft, imperceptible rain of dust from some distant catastrophe had been settling quietly on the blaring, exposed city. The earth was on fire again; at any moment, Tom thought, the streets would begin to bubble and spit and hiss.

The block-square building of the office was a hot brown pile of burnt-cinder bricks. The small lawn in front, slashed with the great white X of sidewalks, looked artificially green, like the matting from a department store's display windows, and at the top of the flagpole a colored rag hung, limp.

"It's a scorcher, ain't it?" the elevator operator said, and yet the calm air of the elevator shaft whispered gently at their passage, ruffling faintly the sheets of the folded newspaper on the elevator operator's bent cane chair, chilling Tom's neck where the wet collar touched his skin.

He crossed the noisy city room to the bank of telephones and called his apartment.

"Hello?" Marjorie said.

"It's me," Tom said. "Everything all right? Is he any better?"

"Oh," Marjorie said. "I can't tell. I think so. Have you been out? I've been thinking you'd call."

"Yes," Tom said. "What about the doctor? What did he say?"

"He hasn't come yet," Marjorie said. "Miss Taylor said he's at the hospital with an emergency."

"Well, I don't understand that," Tom said. He wanted to argue with somebody. "He was supposed to be there at the apartment a half-hour ago. Did she say what hospital?"

"No," said Marjorie. "I don't think it's anything to worry about. It's probably just one of those summer flu things. He hasn't thrown up any more."

"I suppose you're right," Tom said. The telephone was slippery in his palm. "Can he still move his neck and everything?"

"Oh, yes," Marjorie said. "I'm sure it isn't anything like that. It's probably just some kind of flu."

"I suppose," Tom said. "Well. Call me after the doctor sees him. I think I'll be in the office."

"All right," Marjorie said. "Is it awfully hot downtown? It's terrible out here. I'll bet it's awful downtown."

"Yes," Tom said. "It's awful. The noon edition says there's no relief in sight."

"It's terrible," Marjorie said. "Try to stay out of the sun as much as you can. If you have to go out why don't you go in a drugstore every few minutes and get a Coke or something?"

"All right," Tom said. "I will. But you call me when the doctor gets there."

"All right," Marjorie said. "I will. Goodbye."

"Goodbye," Tom said, and hung up.

"What did Pond have?" Thompson said. "Anything?" He stood at Tom's elbow, pot-bellied, hairy forearms protruding mightily from his short-sleeved shirt, his jowls black with his heavy beard, his eyes red-rimmed and impatient. "What was it? An accident?"

"Woman killed her husband," Tom said. "He wanted her to get in the sack so she grabbed his shotgun."

"Where?" Thompson said, looking at the clock on the wall. Tom told him.

"Over there?" Thompson looked down at Tom. "Some of those slum characters? What was a guy like that doing owning a shotgun? What kind was it?"

"I don't know," Tom said. "Just an old double-barrel."

"It doesn't make sense," Thompson said, looking at the clock again. "Anything else to it? Give it to me in takes." He went back to the city desk and sat down at the rim among a dozen other men.

"Frank Kozciewski, 43, an unemployed dishwasher, was shot and killed this afternoon in an apartment at 1402½ Cherry Street," Tom wrote. "Police arrested his wife, Mrs. Mary Kozciewski, of the same address, on a charge of murder."

A copy boy appeared and Tom pulled the sheet from the typewriter and handed it to him.

"Mrs. Kozciewski told Detective Lieutenant Charles Pond the shooting was unintentional.

" 'He began to abuse me and refused to leave me alone,' the attractive, 30-year-old brunette said. 'I didn't realize my husband's shotgun was loaded. I took it out of the closet and pointed it at him and told him not to come near me. He cursed me and then the gun went off.'

"Lt. Pond said the woman blamed the city's current heat wave for the shooting.

"Funeral arrangements have not been completed."

The copy boy appeared again and Tom gave him the sheet of paper, then leaned back in his chair.

Probably it was nothing more than some sort of summer flu, like Marjorie said. Weather like this would be certain to bring all sorts of germs out of the ground, out of the walls, out of the very air. Germinating heat lay solid in the city room, enclosing him in wool. You could get all wet with perspiration and then sit down in a hallway in a draft, or something. Kids never knew any better than not to do things like that. Sometimes their ignorance seemed willful and perverse, determined stupidity, but of course it wasn't. They just didn't know any better. The things you had to learn in order to live! He had never realized how many until they had the child, watching him, that painfully slow accretion of facts which must seem totally unrelated, like rules of grammar in a foreign language, facts which piled up incomprehensibly against the blank consciousness like driftwood against a dead log, some floating off again, some remaining.

"What the hell is this about 'the city's current heat wave'?" Thompson said. The scorn in his voice was a palpable thing: you could pick it up and handle it, weigh it, toss it from hand to hand. He held the sheets of Tom's story out in front of his belly.

"That's what she said," Tom said. "I guess it's so hot they got short-tempered or something."

"You didn't say that," Thompson said. He dropped the sheets on Tom's desk. "You said the heat shot her husband." He walked back to the city desk and sat down impatiently, scraping the chair noisily and angrily.

No, Tom thought, rolling fresh copy paper into his typewriter, I said *she* said the heat wave shot him, damn your niggling soul. He rewrote the story.

"Lt. Pond said the woman blamed 'short tempers' caused by the city's current heat wave for the shooting.

" 'We just got on each other's nerves,' she said.

"Funeral arrangements have not been completed."

He took the sheets to the city desk and put them down at Thompson's elbow.

"Yeah," Thompson said. He picked up the sheets and slung them neatly into a wire basket in the center of the big desk. "Maybe it'll make the home edition. That held it up just too long."

Tom returned to his desk and sat down. He looked at the clock above the telegraph desk: thirty minutes more. He got up and walked to the telephone bank.

"Hello?" said Marjorie.

"Me again," Tom said. "Has the doctor come?"

"No," Marjorie said. "Not yet. I guess he's still at the hospital. Maybe there's been a big wreck or something."

"Maybe," Tom said. He felt helpless. "There always is." It was the Fourth of July weekend. "Probably a lot of kids showing up at every hospital in town with powder burns," he said. "How is he? Can you see any change?"

"No," Marjorie said. "I think he's all right, though. He wanted some of his books."

"Well," Tom said. "I guess it's probably all right."

"I think so," Marjorie said. "It's probably just this awful heat. If he's still feeling better when you get home, why don't we drive out to the park after dinner? Maybe it would be cooler out there, and he wants some sparklers."

"All right," Tom said. "There'll be an awful jam out there, though. Everybody'll have the same idea."

"I know," Marjorie said. "But maybe not. At least we can get some fresh air."

"All right," Tom said. "I'll be home after while."

"I thought we'd just have some salad," Marjorie said. "Are you coming straight home?"

"Yes," Tom said. "I'm coming straight home. Why?"

"Oh, I just thought," Marjorie said. "I thought you might get involved with some of the fellows, or something."

"No," Tom said. "I won't. I'll come on home as soon as I can."

"I don't mean you can't if you want to," Marjorie said.

"I know," Tom said. "You know I quit that. I'll be home as soon as I can."

"All right," Marjorie said. "Do you want to stop and get some beer? Maybe a can of beer would make you feel better when you get home."

"No, no," Tom said. He looked at the clock. "I don't want any. I'll be home a soon as I can."

"All right," Marjorie said. "Goodbye." She hung up.

The arc of water in the electric drinking fountain was warm. Tom held the button down, waiting for the stream to turn chilly. He jiggled two salt tablets from the dispenser on the wall and swallowed them, then drank from the stream. How pleasant it would be in the mountains, on the cold, damp rocks along a cold stream, a real stream, unpolluted, running from the snows.

"You better take off," Thompson said. He was waiting to use the water cooler. "Two minutes after five."

"I guess you're right," Tom said. He stepped aside and Thompson bent over the fountain. The back of his neck was red.

The boy seemed much better. He lay on their bed, his body small in shorts against the broad whiteness, surrounded by brightly colored books. Tom felt the boy's forehead while Marjorie watched from the doorway.

"He feels cool," Tom said. "Didn't the doctor ever even call?"

"No," Marjorie said. "I called Miss Taylor twice and she said he was tied up at the hospital. Maybe he'll try to come by tonight."

"The hell with him," Tom said. "I think he feels fine." He looked down at the five-year-old. "How do you feel? Do you feel better?"

"Sure," the boy said, grinning, fidgeting with the books. "I feel swell. Did you get me any sparklers?"

"I'll get you some later," Tom said. "We'll go out to the park after dinner and you can light them up. Okay?"

"Sure," the boy said. "When? Right now?"

"After we eat," Tom said. "It won't be long."

They sat balanced at the kitchen table, eating the tuna salad while the people on the radio hurled insults and the audience guffawed. It really was too hot for anything but a cold salad: Marjorie said she was worn out with the heat and the thought of cooking something was just too much and Tom said, yes, and this was the only way to have tuna, in a salad like this, stuffed into a gutted tomato. It tasted better that way than any other way, he said. He opened the refrigerator without getting up from his chair, took out the milk carton and poured a little into his coffee. They sat opposite each other, the table between them, perfectly balanced, like a line drawing done in stiff wire.

"Did you remember to bring home a paper?" Marjorie asked, watching as he finished the salad.

"I forgot," Tom said, chewing.

"Oh, well," she said. "What happened today? Anything interesting?"

"The same old stuff," Tom said. "A woman killed her husband down at Fourteenth and Cherry. They're having more trouble in North Africa. I guess the war is just a matter of time."

"Oh, Tom," Marjorie said. "Don't say that."

"A long time, maybe," he said. "But inevitable."

"I don't see why," she said. "Life can be so wonderful. What gets into people?"

Tom shook his head.

"I don't know," he said. "You want to leave the dishes?"

The air blowing through the car windows cooled their skins, but the mohair of the seats was prickly and still held some of the day's heat. As they neared the park the traffic thickened and slowed, until the cars crawled in second gear.

"We'll never be able to get in," Tom said. "The place will be crammed full."

"What about my sparklers?" the boy said from the back seat.

"Don't worry," Tom said. "We'll find a place."

"Sure we will, hon," Marjorie said to the boy. "You just be patient."

"There's a fireworks stand up ahead, I think," Tom said. "I'll try and get over to the curb. They don't let those jerks sell them inside the park."

They were honked at, but they pulled over to the curb, a hundred feet beyond the fireworks stand.

"I'll go," Tom said. "You wait here."

He got out of the car and walked back along the parkway. It was much cooler outside of the car and, now that he was not driving, the flow of traffic through the dusk looked soothing, the metal of the cars cooling in the evening air after the paint-blistering day.

The fireworks stand was made of raw, white two-by-four scaffolding, draped with brown canvas on three sides. A naked light bulb burned inside above the shelves of garishly colored fireworks and a man in a sport shirt stood behind the rough pine counter, leaning on it. He wore a synthetic panama hat with a black and yellow band around it, an imitation of the Palm Beach sportsman of several seasons past, and round glasses in stainless steel frames bit into the oily, bony ridge of his nose.

"Yes, sir," he said. "Fireworks?"

"A couple of boxes of sparklers," Tom said.

"All right, sir," the man said jauntily. He put the flat packages on the counter. "And what else? Skyrockets? Roman candles? Cherry bombs?"

"That's all," Tom said.

"Okay," the man said, looking at Tom. "Four bits."

Damn it, Tom thought, walking toward the car. What do I care about the Fourth of July? How did we ever develop such a stupid custom? Has there always been a gunpowder surplus?

"Here," he said, handing the packages through the window to the boy. "Don't open them now. Wait until we get out of the car."

"Can I light one?" the boy said. He held the packages excitedly, shaking them to hear the sparklers rattle.

"Later," Tom said. "I'll light them for you when we get out of the car."

"I wish you'd look at that traffic," Marjorie said. "It's a solid stream."

"It's this heat, I guess," Tom said. "Everybody's trying to get a little air."

"We'll never be able to get into the park," Marjorie said. "Wouldn't you just know that everybody would drive out here tonight?"

"Well," Tom said. He looked at the traffic. "We're going to have a hell of a time even getting away from the curb," he said. "They're bumper to bumper as far as I can see."

"You promised me!" the boy said.

"Don't get excited," Tom told him, bending over to peer into the dark interior of the car. "We'll light the sparklers. Just keep your shirt on."

"He's so excited," Marjorie said.

"Why don't we just get out right here?" Tom said. "There's plenty of grass. We can light the sparklers for him and by the time they're all gone maybe the traffic will have thinned out. All right?"

He spread the blanket on the grass of the parkway for Marjorie. The first sparkler was lighted and they sat on the blanket, watching the boy's dim figure running back and forth on the grass, violently waving the hot, white crackle above his head.

"It looks so pretty in the dark," Marjorie said. "He enjoys them so."

"Yes," Tom said. The small flare whipped back and forth in the darkness, like Disney's Tinkerbell, of almost insupportable brightness.

"That beats me about that doctor," Tom said. "You'd think he'd at least call."

"I'll bet they've had a time today," Marjorie said. "Thank heaven there wasn't anything really wrong with him. He can't hurt himself on the sparkler, can he?"

"No," Tom said. "Not as long as he doesn't grab hold of the hot end. Don't touch it near the fire!" he called to the boy.

The sparkler halted its mad flight and remained motionless, sputtering, suspended in the night.

"What?" the boy said.

"Don't touch the end with the fire on it," Tom said. "It gets hot. You'll burn yourself."

"All right," the boy said. The sparkler began moving again.

"I think it's getting a little cooler," Marjorie said. "Honestly, this weather! It's much worse than it gets back home."

"I suppose the humidity is worse," Tom said.

"I suppose so," Marjorie said. "But you'd think it would be the other way around. We were only about two hundred miles from the Gulf, back home."

"I don't know," Tom said. "It's something to do with the wind currents, I guess."

"Does it get this hot in the East?" Marjorie asked him, and he said, yes, it did.

"I suppose it gets hot everywhere except in the mountains," he said.

"Yes," Marjorie said. "You know," she said after a silence, "I was thinking today about the rose garden, back in Waco. It's so cool there, even in the summertime. It's out in the park, with a fountain and a pool playing in it all the time. And such roses!"

"You never mentioned it before," Tom said. "Did you go there a lot?"

"Oh, yes," Marjorie said. He could not see her face. "When I was little we used to go out there on picnics a lot, and then when I was older, in high school, sometimes we'd all go out there in a bunch, after a dance, early in the morning. We'd have something to eat downtown after the dance and then all go out there together and take off our shoes and stockings and run around on the grass, in the dew. Just acting silly. The dew was just as heavy as rain on the grass, and cold! you could hardly believe it would be that cold, the dew was."

She was silent, sitting on the blanket in the darkness. They could not see each other.

"It sounds like a nice place," Tom said.

"Yes," Marjorie said. "It was. We used to go out there a lot."

The grass was city grass: they were at least a half-mile from the park, sitting on the blanket.

"Life," Tom said vaguely and tiredly, and stopped. A yellow glow was growing behind him somewhere, drawing Marjorie's seated figure out of the darkness, illumining her soft features, her shoulders, the details of her dress, and glinting on the metal of the car beside them.

"My heaven!" Marjorie said, scrambling to her feet. "Oh, Tom!"

He turned: the bottom of the rear wall of the canvas fireworks stand was fringed with fire, halfway up; a yellow, reddish, curling line of flame which burst, as Tom looked, into a puffball of flame and mushroomed outward. The canvas, Tom thought, paraffin sizing on the canvas.

He was up and running toward the burning stand, but the boy collided against his knees, screaming, and Marjorie was kneeling against his legs, crying and shrieking.

"My sparkler!" the boy said. "It burned me! My hand is hurting! I threw my sparkler away!" speaking at this incredible time with precision and as he had been taught, while beyond them the fireworks stand was engulfed in fire and the frenzied figure of its attendant leaped in front of it, shouting and slapping his hands at the flames amid the sputtering crackle of firecrackers going off in packages.

"Are you hurt?" Tom said. "Get him in the car! Is he hurt?"

"Just his hand, I think," Marjorie said, crying. She picked up the boy. "Oh, Tom!" she said, running toward the car. A skyrocket whistled viciously over their heads and burst twenty feet above the stream of cars, its colored balls of fire dropping instantly onto the metal, sputtering and breaking. And then more skyrockets, some rising into the night sky, some bursting inside the flames and scattering colored balls over the dancing man, and Roman candles puffing, squirting fire across the grass, and the explosions of the heavier fireworks, muffled and terrible.

The man was screaming when Tom got to him. Probably he had been screaming for some time, but only now could he be heard. Tom grabbed him around the waist and tore him from the blazing heap of the stand, wrestling him fifty feet along the parkway before they tripped and fell. The hat went rolling but Tom grabbed it and began beating at the flames on the man's charred forearms and chest, at the running, smoking flames in his trousers. The hat knocked off the blackened, shattered spectacles and the man, screaming steadily in a high, frightened voice, pawed at his eyes with his crisp, webbed fingers. In the eyesockets were not eyes but bloody pulps of some sort, and Tom knocked the man's hands away with the man's hat, shouting, "Damn you, keep your hands away, keep your Goddamned hands away!" It seemed obvious that the man's eyeballs had been torn loose in the sockets by the blazing impact of something from the fireworks stand, and Tom stood over him in the night, straddling the burning man as people ran screaming and shouting and the car horns blared unceasingly, slapping the hat at the man and thinking, My God, how can we ever survive, and why do we even want to so much?

nightwatch
at vernal equinox

❊   "You can do ennythang, but keep offa mah blue suede shoes!" shouts the man in the jukebox. "You can burn down mah house, you can steal mah cah, you can drink mah lickah fum a ole fruit jah!"

It is a song: he shouts it from a tight, excited throat against the frantic drumming of the rural guitars. The hidden record spinning in the bloated, winking jukebox blasts the walls of the bus station café, walls and ceiling shiny with old white enamel and the congealed grease given off by a million hamburgers; the sound bursts along the counters and booms and rattles in the glass cases of dead pie slices, crusted cake segments and soggy, oily sweet rolls.

The listless waitresses stand in the jukebox roar, their thin arms folded across their flat chests, their pimpled faces sad, stern, empty, their bodies draped in nylon uniforms. The counter top is formica, the ketchup and mustard bottles are polyethylene, the jukebox a geological age of laminated, scrolled and twisted plastics. The menus are slick in envelopes of heavy cellophane, the counter bears islands of stiffened Pliofilm turrets, scratched and blurred, squatting guard over more pie slices and cake hunks. Along the

93

floor, lapping around the pedestals of the counter stools and the heavy base of the jukebox, running back into the darkness at the rear of the café, where the toilets are, is the dark green linoleum, filmy, curling, scaly around the pedestals.

"I'm waiting for a climax," says a man seated at the counter. He is fortyish, burly, heavy-shouldered, with thick black hair brushed back from his forehead. His hands cradle a mug of coffee, and on the backs of his hands the hair is black and curling and thick. He wears a brown suit, brown shoes, and a muffler in place of a necktie. The muffler is of Paisley silk, the sort of muffler one saw twenty years ago, smooth from his chin to the buttoned V of his suit coat. On his dark, heavy, closely shaved jowls the man wears rouge, and on his mouth lipstick glares against his dark skin.

"I'm waiting for a climax," he says, not saying it to anyone in particular, staring straight ahead between two waitresses. They do not look at him: one slowly lifts an arm and carefully, as though avoiding pain, picks her teeth with a toothpick. The waitresses on the night watch don't listen to anything other than orders for hamburgers, pie, cake or coffee. They do not hear the word "climax," do not wonder at the man's meaning, do not suspect him of speaking of sex, since they have another word for that part of sex but never use it, since they have never experienced it and cannot, except to please their men and repeat by rote some faintly recalled dirty jokes, even believe in it.

And they are right. The man is not talking about that: he is just waiting, waiting, as he has waited in the midwestern town's bus station café for how many nights, waiting for the buses pounding down the bricks of U.S. Highway 81, pounding out of the night, through the sleeping countryside and into the dozing, fitful city, a barren city of grain elevators, department stores, the hot iron and grit and slam of railroad yards, and the people, midwestern people.

But these are not the midwestern people here in the café of the bus station. The people, the good folks, are at home asleep, or anyway at home, packed in the red and brown brick buildings near the center of town, ranked in the white frame houses farther out, and arranged in the ranch-style ramblers, farther out still. The farther you live from the center of town the less likely it is that you have ever seen the interior of the bus station or its café. The night people are unknown to the owners of the ranch-style ramblers, who have their own problems and disasters: obesity, fallen wombs, perforated stomach linings, sleeplessness in the nights and drowsiness in the afternoons, breast lumps, monstrous uterine cauliflowers and the occasional child who is not quite right in the head, the matching automatic washers and dryers in the new pastel shades, the walk-in deep freezers, the problems of space, of where to store things.

In one of the ramblers lives a young woman with husband and children. In college she did many things: she read some of Franz Kafka, for instance, but mistook him for a science fiction writer. She is fascinated by grotesques but has never, to her knowledge, known any. Although the state has gone Republican in every election since it was admitted to the union she always votes Democratic and is a Democratic worker, giving teas for lady Democrats, organizing discussion groups, attending night classes in the humanities at the city's university, interested in high fidelity phonograph records, a subscriber to *The Reporter* magazine, a giver of patio barbecue dinners in the California manner, a singer of American folk songs with her husband and children, a writer of protest letters to the city's newspaper, a subscriber to symphony concerts, a follower of much of John Dewey's philosophy, a smiling believer in the newer versions of psychoanalysis, an indignant racist in reverse, intellectually anti-Communist, a foe of private power projects on the public domain, and not too certain of her attitude toward the distant and historic Moral Rearmament movement. Her husband keeps an atomizer full of vermouth with which he makes his celebrated martinis, earns twelve thousand dollars a year and is extremely interested in the Great Books program. The city is not really their kind of city, but there are the children and their little friends to be thought of, and the children have a subscription to the *National Geographic* and own all of the Little Golden Books.

So the night people in the bus station are far, far from the rambler folk. Some of the students at the university are aware of this distance, and they come to the bus station café after a night of drinking cheap whiskey or alcohol and grape juice. They want to see life as it is really lived, stripped of all illusion. They feel, after a course in the university's humanities sequence (modeled on that of the University of Chicago), that something is wrong: for a time they are uncomfortable with their illusions and those of the parents who are supporting them, and they come to the bus station café to see life without illusions, to lose, if possible, their own. The town is not large; the bus station café must serve as their Montparnasse, their North Beach, their Greenwich Village, their underground. It never works the other way: the night people do not go out into the suburbs to peer through picture windows into lighted living rooms, to finger the chill metal of cars in the nighttime driveways. Very probably they would be arrested if they did, but there's more to it than that: they don't want to go to the suburbs. It is this fact, more than any other thing they know about the night people, which disturbs and attracts the students. Is this what happens in an illusionless world? Peculiar!

Because the students are in transition, spies and yet not really spies, thieves of experience and yet not really thieves. They have not yet suffered that corrosion which will eat away their passion for intangibles and clear them out, making room for objects, for things, machinery, appliances, insurance policies, memberships, the older identity. At present all they want of that identity is new clothes, a motor car and spending money, as it is called, and these are not the same as the other appliances and machinery. These are for sex, they say: without them there can be no sex, since their girls have not yet been cleared out either and so will not go to a motel or a hotel to do the things they will do in parked motor cars. Conversely, the waitresses in the bus station café will not do the things in a motor car they will do in a motel or a hotel, but most of the students are not aware of that, and in any case the waitresses would not suffice. As part-time spies and thieves the students find the waitresses a little too obvious, not mysterious, as are the girls in the parked motor cars. Occasionally a student couples with a waitress or a prostitute, but the experience is never entirely satisfactory. It is too straightforward, too well illuminated, not like the movies at all: the wrestling in the parked car with its invisible culmination is more like the movies, since the radio plays its background music and the darkness is glamorous and kind to errors.

But the experience in the parked cars does not strike the students with the blow of reality, since reality must be unpleasant: otherwise, they believe, it is fraudulent, middle-class. The experiences in the parked cars exist in darkness, unreal, without sociological coordinates. Here, in the bus station café, is reality, think the students, since reality is, after all, life stripped of all illusion. That nakedness makes reality a little dangerous, of course: the students are rather nervous in the café, they talk among themselves in low voices, watching the café customers furtively, nudging each other when the man in rouge and lipstick says he is waiting for a climax. But the students are ignored. To the waitresses and the customers there is nothing odd or vulnerable about the students whatever. They are recognized as fellows from the college out south, no more, and the students come to the café to sit and watch and listen, drinking the bitter coffee to clear their heads of alcohol, perhaps wasting their substances, perhaps not. It is too early to tell.

The students are not concerned with substance yet, unless their substance is to be their sex and the totems of their sex: the spending money and the motor cars now, the washer-dryer later in pastel pink, the battery-operated martini mixing rods which still lie somewhere in their futures. The professors at the university do not alarm the students much about the future: it is somebody else's future the professors are talking about, and the students are not very interested in somebody else's future. There has been too much of that sort of interest already, they tell each other in the dormitories and the beer joints, and that sort of interest has no real use whatever, so the professors drone away without alarming the students, and the students don't alarm the professors. Of course there is always one professor who is alarmed, and each semester he manages to alarm one or two students, but no more than that. He tells the students they enter as cabbage heads and they will leave as cabbage heads, but the students smile at the professor's accent, which is French. Except for one or two students who don't smile at all, but frown, and chew on pencil ends, and shift uneasily on the varnished wooden chairs in quiet, new alarm. Sometimes they raise their hands to argue, or stop the professor in the hall, and rarely, very rarely, they are so upset and gutted with alarm they go out and get drunk, or insult their parents, or join the ministry. One time, several years ago, the professor moved one girl to hopeless prostitution with his lectures on *The Brothers Karamazov,* and the girl was seen no more on campus. The professor remembers her: he thinks about her often, rather proudly, and sometimes tells new instructors about her, but never the dean.

Things like that are pretty unusual, though, and the professor who is alarmed knows they are unusual, and contents himself with less, out of necessity. Once, when he had worked himself into a state of terrible ecstasy and thunder over *War and Peace* on the final lecture of the course, he found the only response to be a question from a boy who wanted to know if they'd be required to know all that for the final examination, and this so enraged the professor that he shouted, yes, they would be required to know it, along with the number of rounds fired at the Battle of Borodino, the number of legs amputated and the number of meters of gauze used in dressing the wounds of the survivors. But he had gone too far, of course: the students smiled, and there were no final examination questions about the Battle of Borodino at all.

Now, on this particular night, when the man at the bus station counter said he was waiting for a climax, at a few minutes past midnight, one of the rambler folk was dying in his ranch-style bungalow out south, three blocks from the rambler where the girl who had read Kafka lay sleepless in her half of the twin beds, thinking of Mrs. Roosevelt, Frank Lloyd Wright and her martini-famous husband, who was in Chicago attending a convention of air-conditioning engineers.

It was a dreadful night for dying, one of the first full nights of the midwestern spring. The smell of grass and damp earth came through the bedroom windows and the birds, despite the late hour, made noises in the budding trees. Still, a rambler owner lay dying in his bedroom, attended by his wife and physician. His son, fourteen years old, sat on the living room couch in pajamas and bathrobe, leafing through a copy of *Motor Age*.

The dying man's wife stood by the bedside in negligee, wrung by sorrow and incomprehension, and faintly troubled by the thought of what might happen to the mattress. She could not prevent the thought: once, long ago, when she and the dying man had first been married, when she was a young housewife, crisp and fresh and sweet-tasting, a door-to-door photographer had died in the apartment next door, just as he was bending over his camera to snap the portrait of the neighbors' children. He had straightened up, gasped, and fallen backward as solidly and terrifically as a collapsing building, and before the police ambulance removed him his sphincter had relaxed and soiled the rug. The wife could not keep this out of her mind, as she sobbed and called the dying man's name.

The dying man was of some importance in the town, a builder of ranch-style ramblers, a planner of residential districts, a respected customer of banks, an outstanding member of the Toast-masters Club, a past state commander of the American Legion, a citizen in every respect. His life had run on ballasted rails, not at all like that of the long-dead door-to-door photographer, who had followed one of those uncertain and insecure callings in which, more often than not, death comes on someone else's property. And that is an awful thing, not to die in your own place, to be, to the last, dependent on harassed, impatient strangers. Your uniqueness cannot survive that.

And so the individuality, the uniqueness of the planner of subdivisions, was being preserved: the borrower of millions of dollars, the earner of hundreds of thousands, the husband, the father, the veteran, was dying at home, decaying in the bedroom of the big ranch-style rambler into a small monument, providing a reference point in the city and the family. He had not been at home, in his bed, this early for many years. He had been, as he said, active in so many organizations, and of course business did not end with the five o'clock whistle, he often said. But he had been a good family man, everyone said. Each Friday night, if he was in the city, he took his wife and son out to dinner. He had done this for many years.

It was always the same. They would be seated in the restaurant, always a quiet, wholesome place where the lighting was too bright and everything looked clean, and they would each be given a menu by the waitress, who always knew them. They would look at the items printed on the menu and the builder would talk to his wife and son:

"All right, now. See anything you like? How about the roast loin of pork with sweet potatoes and marshmallow sauce and chef's tossed green salad? You get a choice of beverage with that. Hot coffee, tea, or milk. Or the breaded veal cutlets with cream sauce, scalloped potatoes and salad Waldorf? Hm? See anything you like? They have iced tea with lemon. Fifteen cents. Hm? Or how about a nice steak? They have the club house with french fried long branch potatoes and a tossed green salad. Two seventy-five. You have a choice of delicious ice-cold tomato juice or a cup of today's soup with that. Chicken and rice with noodles, cup ten cents, bowl twenty-five. Hm? Get whatever you want, now."

He was a good man, perhaps, but it had been difficult to measure him. He had been the husband, the businessman, the father. It had been difficult to measure him.

And now he was dying, with many projects unfinished, many things left undone on this full night of spring. His voice mechanism had failed when the heart within him gave that terrible, awesome lurch and gurgle, and he lay on the bed in his underwear, looking up at the doctor and at his wife, unable to speak, smelling the damp earth smell on the air which moved softly through the bedroom windows, since it would not be necessary to turn on the air-conditioning units and seal up the house for a month or more. The heat was at least a month away. Of course, the air-conditioning units were expensive to install and to operate, but they made possible sleep in summer, and they made housekeeping much easier, too: the dust couldn't get in. The time was coming when every new house would include an air-conditioning unit as matter of factly as garbage disposal units were now included, there was no doubt about it. The ramblers would be air-conditioned. When you could offer an air-conditioned home for eleven or twelve five, why, that would be something, all right. Or even thirteen five.

Lying in his bedroom near the center of the enormous, rolling, soft, jagged and blank continent, the builder thought thus of fortifying against that intense, sinister heat which lies on the plains in summer, whether to help others to withstand nature or simply to make money for himself it was difficult to say, since it was much too complicated for such simple measurement: proud of the ranch-style homes, the subdivisions on serpentined streets planted with fully-grown trees from nurseries, hard and committed forever against the experimental in architecture, the "or-

ganic" as the great experimenter called it. And a thousand miles to
the west the experimenter himself lay in his great camp of stone,
wood and canvas in the desert, in the fitful sleep of the very old;
and the desert camp was the generator, the source of all the split-
level ramblers, as the dying man was of the youth who read *Motor
Age* in the living room. A beautiful Bedouin encampment of stone,
wood and canvas from which the assault was mounted each
morning in the desert, the trumpet and campaign of architecture-
made man, warring with the builder's man-made architecture,
houses against homes.

The girl who had once read Kafka couldn't sleep. She lay on
her half of the twin beds in a pink nylon nightgown, her body
fresh and warm and soft, her mind urgent with indecision. The
legends of gods and of Christ had been invented to make man feel
guilty, and yet it began to look as though psychoanalysis was not a
satisfactory substitute. There was always another guilt lying beneath the one the analyst pulled off. She was not aware of any
particularly strong feelings of guilt in herself, nor had she ever
visited an analyst, but the subject was interesting, and important.
Many of her friends had suffered *post partem* breakdowns or
crackups, because they had failed to keep their minds occupied.
They had stagnated into housewives, and when the pressures came
that was not enough, she knew. They should have kept themselves
interested in important things. Her husband always agreed with
her. The town really was not their kind of place at all, in spite of
the fact that the nation's most famous psychiatric clinic was only
sixty miles away. The *post partem* cases whose parents could
afford it were sent there, where they made costume jewelry from
sterling silver wire, as they regained their equilibrium in the
occasional company of disturbed movie stars. The clinic was an
annex of the good life and the staff was remarkably successful in
returning rehabilitated housewives to the subdivisions. The returnees were encouraged to talk freely of their experiences to those
of their friends who had not yet been to the clinic. It was even

suggested smilingly that the use of such expressions as "When I was in the bughouse" or "While the headshrinkers had me" would help to remove the embarrassment the friends were sure to feel in the returnees' presence. There was nothing to be ashamed of: the staff emphasized that quite strongly.

And of course there was not, the girl who had once read Kafka told herself. The fact that the clinic's staff would even feel it necessary to point that out showed you how this part of the country really wasn't what you'd like it to be.

Impatiently, she rose from her airfoam mattress and walked to the open window. She stood looking out into the darkness, a gentle breeze pressing the pink nylon against her body. The smell of the night made her sad, nostalgic for some time or place she couldn't name; she thought of seacoasts and forests, of wild birds migrating, of surf bursting on rocks she'd never seen. She smelled the hot pine gum of faraway woods, the dust of deserts and southwestern towns, the perfume of bakeries at midnight in strange cities. Life, it seemed to her, was being lived elsewhere, not here in her city. She felt that her ideas and interests were false, second-hand: she was only a spectator, and terribly removed from the spectacle. She sighed, she ran her fingers through her hair and thought, I'll go out for a drive. I can't sleep, I'll go out for a drive, and guiltily, she dressed.

It was a night when sailors walk the streets and giggle, calling to the girls, sailors combing their hair with combs they take from blouse pockets bulged with cigarette packs, saying, "Hey! Where ya goin'?" whipping the combs through their hair and then restoring them to tiny pockets in the blouses.

I'll get old and nothing will ever happen to me, thought the girl who had once read Kafka, driving slowly down the main street, watching the sailors, the delivery boys, the soldiers, the salesmen and the girls. It's Saturday night for everybody but me, she thought, listening to the music on the car radio. Cats moved toward black alleys, as certain and contemptuous as Arabs, and the store windows spilled blue-white light onto the gritty sidewalks to throw crumpled candy wrappers into crisp relief. Objects filled the windows: synthetic silk stockings displayed on clear plastic legs kicked and died in the cold fluorescence; cellulose fibers from the giant molecules were fluffed to look like fur, and one window was crammed with hideously tortured handbags of simulated Mexican leather, burned and scarred with imitation Mexican designs, as shiny as varnish, as slick as grease. Above the popcorn stand an electric bug killer snapped and popped, electrocuting moths and June bugs: ten thousand corpses lay around the popcorn vendor's feet as he ladled hot coconut oil over the swollen kernels.

The girl in the car drove on toward the bus station café and passed it and crossed the Santa Fe tracks and turned onto the bridge, crossing the river and picking up speed, hoping to catch up with something. On the horizon lightning glared, swelling and fading, far away and silent, playing in the terrible beginning thunderheads of summer's coming, at thirty thousand feet.

And oh, dear reader, how pleasant it would be if the girl who couldn't sleep had perhaps picked up a sailor, or dropped by the bus station café for coffee and saved the lipsticked man who was waiting for a climax, or had met the students and they had all resolved one another, leading to divorce, to scandal and farewell to the rambler and the vermouth atomizer! Would that be pleasant? Or perhaps the girl should've found that life was busy in the city, along with death, and discovered a June bug's oily corpse in a bag of hot popcorn, and thought of her children, those devoted readers of the Golden Books, and returned to her airfoam bed a wiser woman with a husband all unknowing at his convention in Chicago, her connubial obligations all intact, ready now to wait, no matter where she was in summer, for compassion to come and fill her up. Would that be pleasant?

Well, that's not the way that summer was, a long five years ago, dear reader: the great old man is dead, and the man who built the ramblers is dead, and his son sells used motor cars in Los Angeles, and there are new students in the bus station café each night, and very often the girl who had read Kafka cannot sleep. She can't understand that sleeplessness, not really: her husband now makes seventeen thousand dollars a year because the rambler builder had been right, almost every home is air-conditioned now, and air-conditioning engineers are doing very well, and the children are doing very well in school (they now get all the Landmark Series instead of the Golden Books), and she has avoided, so far, the great psychiatric clinic sixty miles away, although it seems a little closer, more accessible and less expensive, each time that summer comes.

motto for a wall

‡‡ That summer coming back from Galveston they had dinner in the Sea Food House on San Jacinto battlefield, the battlefield like a park of rolling green grass, closely and carefully mowed, and the Sea Food House a rambling, splintered wooden building surrounded with verandas on rotting supports.

They ate stuffed crabs, the mother and the father and the boy, in the midst of a hundred white, threaded tablecloths, and the crab shells piled up on the table as the smiling Negroes brought them until at last one shell slid from the table and cracked on the floor, making them laugh. The father and the son said it was the mother's shell which fell, but she denied it, and they laughed and laughed, while the Negroes watched them, smiling and pouring ice water.

After dinner they walked in the cool blue evening over the battlefield, trying to read bronze tablets and gazing solemnly at the clumsy field guns still in place or pretending to be still in place, and in the distance, moving queerly through the grass, the lights and superstructure of a freighter glided silently in the Ship Channel, going up to Houston. In the cool air over the cut grass came the smell of tar and salt from the ship, the wild, exciting foreign smell on San Jacinto battlefield, and when they climbed into the hot sedan smelling of dust they were restless, and weary.

When they got to Houston the boy's skin was swollen and lumpy with an itching rash and as the mother daubed the lumps with a white drugstore liquid she said it must have been the crabs but the father thought it was swimming in the sea at Galveston. They spread a sheet over the back seat and the boy lay on the cool fabric, feeling the prickling plush beneath it as they drove through the night with all the windows down, the air smelling of cold wood smoke which soothed his fevered, lumpy skin. He thought of the smell of tar, and driving through the night from Galveston, and the ordered quiet of San Jacinto battlefield like a huge, rolling golf green. The freighter in the Ship Channel was the first he'd ever seen like that, so large and moving, and when they got home everything was intolerable, all dust and sun, and four hundred miles from the sea.

He smelled the sun and dust everywhere, he tasted it, a heated, sweaty penny on his tongue, and dry dust on everything; he hated motor cars because they were so dry and dusty and searing to the touch when they stood in the sun. He hiked with his friends in the woods and they sat in cool, damp creek bottoms, dreaming, and almost every day they killed a rattlesnake, a copperhead or a moccasin, and one day a coral snake like a necklace of colored beads, lashing them with sticks or firing little twenty-twos. Each time they saw death on the clay before them and he knew it, but it wasn't enough; he flicked at coiling rattlers with his stick, straightening their heavy, resisting bodies while they undulated in buzzing fury, striving to coil and strike at his bare, sunburned legs, their jaws unhinged in hate, their white mouths glaring in the sun. But that wasn't enough.

Naples is a pretty good town, all right, the cook said, if you stay away from the waterfront. You know what they're like down there? They live in caves, he said, and he spat a messy string of tobacco juice over the rail and they watched it fall away behind them and drop into the boiling, hissing sea. That's a fact, said the cook. Those bastards live in caves down there like a bunch of lizards and at night they come out and prowl and sneak around, and they're no damned good at all, I tell you. You stay away from the waterfront. You go up on the Vomero, up high, it's where people live in houses and it's quiet, with bars on the corners. You'd almost think you were home, up there. But stay away from those bastards in the caves. They've been living there forever, nobody knows why, and they're mean, cutthroat bastards. Gimme a hand with this crap over the fantail, said the cook, and they tossed the broken crates and emptied the cans of garbage into the wake as the ship beat on across the empty sea. All you'll get on that waterfront is blue balls, the cook said. You just keep going on up where it's high, you'll think you're back home. Bella Napoli my ass, the cook said, and he walked back into the galley. There were grease stains around his hip pockets where he wiped his hands and the flesh of his neck looked red and tender, as though it had been steamed or boiled.

They passed Gibraltar in the afternoon and that night the electrician locked himself in the linen stores and set fire to a stack of sheets.

From the terrace of the café on the hill they could look down at Pozzuoli harbor and the curve of stone buildings, the color of an old circus lion, lying along the shore in the yellow sunlight. The flat sea was cobalt blue near the shore. Farther out it was the color of slate and far out in the haze they could see the smoke of freighters, coasting toward the north.

I come over here because of Spain, Swenson said. You wouldn't believe it, but that was why I come. He sat staring over the iron railing down at Pozzuoli harbor, his big hand lying on the metal table top, curled loosely around his glass. He had very thick and bushy eyebrows and his strong face was marked with small black dots in the pores around his eyes and nose, as though black powder had exploded in his face. I worked the ore boats out of Duluth and then I had a country store up in the woods, up in the lake country, he said. I was a tough bastard then. Every Friday night I drove into Park Rapids to the liquor store and got drunk on California vino and then I raised hell with everybody. They only had one cop and he was scared of me, so I really raised hell. And then I started getting in arguments about the stuff in the papers and I'd always been a good union man so I went to New York and signed on. I was going to jump ship and pay somebody to take me across the mountains but hell, the more I thought about it the less I understood it. You know, sometimes it was hard to remember which was which. I went on a real tear in Marseilles and when I come to I was in Lyons, lying in that bare-assed park across from the railroad station, and I come on back to the ship. I guess I just don't understand all that stuff, but that was what I come over here for, to go to Spain. I used to think I was a pretty tough bastard, Swenson said. What do you say, kid? Shall we get another bottle?

How many times do I have to tell you I been here before, the cook asked him. They were walking in the middle of a narrow alley in the darkness and the cook was drunk, and there were rustling sounds in the darkness ahead and behind them. You young punks, you think you know so Goddamned much, the cook said loudly. Do you know how long I been at sea? I been at sea twenty-two years, the cook said, and you think I don't know where I am? I was at sea before you was born.

I know that, the boy said.

You don't know anything, the cook said. You didn't have to come if you didn't want to.

You said you'd show me back to the ship, he told the cook. I don't know where it is any more.

Jesus Christ, take a streetcar, the cook said. You young punks don't know a Goddamned thing. Where do you think you are, China?

There aren't any, the boy said. It must be too late.

It's about nine o'clock, shouted the cook, but the boy said that in about six hours it would be nine o'clock. It's three in the morning, he said.

The cook argued with him as they walked noisily through the black alley and finally the cook stopped and held his lighter up before a huge wooden door and began pounding on the wood with his feet. An old Italian opened a smaller door set in the big door and shouted at them, but the cook crashed past the old man and the boy followed the cook, leaving the old man still shouting at the door. They hurried through another door, he following the cook in blind panic, and rushed up a flight of stone steps and through still another door and stopped in the room beyond it. Three women were sitting at a table in the room, eating spaghetti and sliced tomatoes.

I'm back, the cook said, and he bent over one of the surprised women and kissed her, placing his right hand quietly and assuredly on her left breast. The women screamed and stood up, knocking over the table, and the cook began shouting and cursing. He seized the arms of the woman he had kissed and shouted into her face until she stopped screaming, then he pulled her after him and left the room. The other women put the table back on its legs and cleaned up the spilled spaghetti and the boy stood there, watching them. The women looked at him and laughed, and then they said something to him, but he shook his head. It was very late and the women looked old. One was pregnant. He stood by the door, waiting for the cook, and the women sat in the chairs, laughing at him.

He wasn't sure, but he thought that was probably enough. He

left the ship in New Orleans and went home on the railroad, sitting up all night in a chair car, the coal dust silting his clothes and his skin and his hair with grit. His parents met him at the station and for a month he slept late and spent the afternoons and nights with his friends. Then his father got him a job as a bank messenger at fifteen dollars a week. Ten months after that he enlisted in the Army because he said he didn't care for the Navy and in 1943 a mortar shell burst near him on the forward slope of Mount Trocchio, near Cassino. He was a survey sergeant with an artillery battalion and the survey crew had been sent out on the forward slope to run a survey although nobody expected to put the guns there. It was just one of those things. He almost bled to death before they got him back to the aid station and when he had time to think about it he wondered if that wasn't nearly enough.

They kept him several days at a general hospital in Capua, waiting. The hospital wasn't too bad. They had taken it over from the Italian army and a lot of Italian equipment was still in it. There was a clumsy obstetrical table out in the courtyard, lying on its side. He thought that only the Italian army would drag around a thing like that and only his army would throw it out in the rain. The hospital was a hollow square around the courtyard and the people with inside rooms had to look out at the table all day long. He never saw anybody in the courtyard because of the rain. Everybody stayed under the gallery if they had to go from one side of the courtyard to the other, and he couldn't see anybody at all, just that absurd contraption of pipes and straps, chrome-plated and dripping all day long. It got on his nerves.

There were two other men in his room but they were bed cases and they didn't talk. He wanted to talk. He didn't think he'd ever wanted to talk as much as he did then, but he couldn't find anybody who seemed just right. The doctors were always in a hurry and he was afraid to say too much in front of the nurses because he knew the kinds of words he was using, they were all using them and he couldn't remember not to use them in front of the nurses. And anyway these were general hospital nurses. The farther he got from the war the worse it was that way, he supposed everybody noticed that. It got more and more like home, as a matter of fact, and that was the last thing he wanted. He thought home was just a V-mail, not even a letter but the photograph of a letter. It was odd, but things seemed to him to be backward, somehow. Home was what he wanted when he was with the battalion but when he started back from the war home wasn't what he wanted at all. He didn't know why that was, but he guessed it was the kind of thing he wasn't supposed to mention.

It was funny about the V-mail. One day the hospital chaplain came into the room. He came around every week, he said. The boy from Texas was sitting on his bed and the other two in the room didn't talk to anybody so the chaplain sat down on the bed with him. The other two didn't even seem to notice the chaplain was there.

The chaplain asked about the arm and then kind of joked around a little, showing the boy he wasn't a prissy type of chaplain, and then they got to talking about religion. The boy felt terrible about that because you just don't do it, of course, but they got into it before he knew it and he didn't sound very cheerful. He could sit up and walk around but he didn't feel very cheerful and the chaplain said he was worried about that. It was a pity, he said, and if he could talk straight from the shoulder he thought the boy was making a mistake and that it would just do more harm than good. We have to take everything as it comes and not complain, the chaplain said, and the boy had to agree with that all right but it didn't make him feel any more cheerful and finally they had kind of an argument about God and the war and then the chaplain handed him a stack of V-mail blanks and told him to write home. The chaplain said he was not taking offense. He was a very healthy-looking man and his breath smelled of wintergreen mints. Right after he went out the door the man in the next bed said Balls! in a perfectly clear voice, but when the boy went over and looked at him he was just lying there with his eyes closed. His lips were chapped so badly that little shreds of flesh bristled on them. He was very sick and breathed through his mouth too much. But the boy thought that was pretty funny about the V-mail. He told the doctor about it and the doctor said yes, the chaplain was a very confident man if he thought you were going to be writing letters with that arm. They had to laugh about that and then the nurses changed the dressings.

They had a German lieutenant on the same floor. He was an artillery observer and his infantry had walked off his mountain without telling him, he said. He was in a tree and when he realized his infantry had gone he started to climb down but an American shot his legs up with a Thompson. He was very bitter against his infantry. You were not supposed to go into his room because he was a prisoner, but everybody did, and it was a cheerful place. Everybody laughed and joked and asked him questions, trying to understand what it was that had brought them from home to this place, but he didn't seem to know. He asked the same questions. He was twenty years old and he hadn't started to shave yet. Even with the American Army food he still had that enemy odor, an unpleasant pork sausage smell, rancid and greasy. It was caused by their rations, and even though he was now eating vienna sausages, spam and powdered eggs, you could smell him when you went into his room. Since everybody wore pajamas and maroon corduroy Army bathrobes you could not tell anybody's rank and so the boy from Texas went into the German's room often, just sitting in a corner and looking at him. The boy was very pleased that he did not hate the German, and when the time came for him to be flown to Africa he was certain that he had learned a great deal: this, he thought, was probably enough.

And so he was calm when he went back to Africa. The hospital was out in the bare, rocky land near Bizerte, closed in by low hills. The sky was heavy and clouded every day, not like an African sky at all, and dead tanks lay rusting in the landscape like piles of iron ore.

He was calm, but after a time he saw that now he probably knew too much for Africa. The hospital was a group of old French barracks and the staff was awfully bored and depressed. The nurses were pinched-looking, short-tempered and frustrated, and the doctors all drank too much. On their days off the doctors took the nurses to the beach and sat drinking, staring out at the empty sea. The war, the world, had gone elsewhere: there was little for them to do here on the hard, empty edge of Africa. The ward boys were thieves: it seemed to the boy from Texas that they had all gone to high school with each other in New York City, and he despised them, as he despised the jumpy, irritable nurses.

He did not like to despise them: in his new knowledge he thought he never wanted to feel strongly again about anything at all, and this emotion bothered him. He finally decided the trouble was that these people had not been outside of the house, somehow; they had stayed at home while he and a few others ventured out into the tornado. They were embarrassed and ashamed before the boy from Texas and the ones like him, and so of course they were cruel and petty, sneakingly vindictive. This was a fine thought, and he marveled at how much he had learned since he had known the cook and the electrician and the man who had wanted to go to Spain. Now, he thought, I am armored forever, and he felt so safe within this new armor that he even began writing home again, crude and clumsy scrawls on the V-mail blanks with his left hand. He was arrogant, of course: the tornado man can never again be one with those who cowered in the storm cellar with the jars of preserved fruit, he thought. He wrote that there was no god and no country, although what he meant to write was that he no longer believed in politics. He put aside his instinctive fear of the doctors and nurses, and when they gave him his Purple Heart he mailed it home with a sarcastic note. He felt wonderfully, marvelously alone, and extremely responsible to himself.

Still, the hospital was a depressing place. He would have to stay there two months, they said, with his arm in a cast, until everything healed and knitted. Each day seemed a week, a year; the hours dragged excruciatingly between meals, and the Red Cross woman ran out of good cigarettes. He was irritated to find himself beginning to feel embarrassed before the ward boys and the nurses and the doctors. His knowledge of the tornado was a fine and awesome thing, unspeakable, untranslatable, but it did not fit into this world: he felt the embarrassment of the accident victim, terribly and painfully wiser than the curious crowd which surrounded him, their clothes clean and whole, their bodies not torn, not bloody. This world expected him to look neat, and the boy from Texas did not feel that he could ever care about looking or feeling neat again. He felt he was superior, yes, but too alien, beyond them but expected to respond, to be responsible to their petty rules and hopes. He could not do it, and he thought with sudden pleasure and surprise of the men in his battalion: he had never liked any of them particularly, but now he saw he loved them because he understood them: they knew the same things he knew and there, in Italy, those were the only things worth knowing. Africa was no longer in the world, and so he escaped from the hospital.

It was not difficult. He bribed a pimple-faced ward boy with fifty dollars in lire and left the hospital in the laundry truck, hidden under a pile of very dirty sheets. The driver let him off at the airfield near Bizerte and he caught a flight within two hours. Nobody asked about the cast: the pilot grinned and winked, and told him to get on board the C-47.

It was not a combat airplane but he felt better and better as they took off and swung out over the motionless sea, knowing that each minute drew him closer to the world he understood and farther from this alien Africa which once had seemed his world when he was fighting there, and when the airplane circled for its landing at Naples he was smiling and happy. He would have no difficulty in catching a ride up to the front, and besides, he thought as the plane settled to earth and the gray, blank hangars rose to shut out the streets and houses and hills of Naples, there was no hurry: the war would last forever, and that was enough; he was twenty years old and he no longer had to look any farther than that.

the man
on the trestle

❖   The first feeling he could remember after it happened
was relief. As he looked at the bloody tangle of flesh and flew the
airplane he was so glad it was over. He trembled with this
unexpected relief, twisting his head to look on all sides for the
fighters, not really believing they would come rushing again,
monstrous in split seconds behind the oily plexiglass. They
wouldn't do that because it had happened and now it wouldn't
have to happen to him again. He had not been an optimist like
the others and so he was entitled to have this happen only once.
He was very glad because it wasn't as painful as he had expected;
it felt as though the back of his hand had been struck with a
hammer and after the first shock of the blow the pain became
duller.

He held the Cub in a shallow dive until he could see the faces
of the truck drivers looking up at him and then leveled out,
tugging carefully at the black rubber grip on the stick with his
middle finger; he glanced at the thumb and forefinger; they were
swollen and throbbing with numbness. The stick came back
firmly, alive, and he flew over the road at seventy miles per hour,

eager for the barley field and almost laughing because in fifteen minutes he would be there and it would all be over. Just like that, all the details, the problems, the planning; the weary effort to keep clean and the search for something to drink each night, all wiped away like a badly written sentence on a blackboard. In its place would be clean lettering, order; they might even fly me home, he thought, and he pushed the throttle forward with his left hand.

Down the valley he sailed, detached from the muddy, inefficient earth with its protracted, never completed toil, aloft in his small universe of linen and duralumin skeleton. Blood dropped slowly from his right hand and spattered on the plywood floorboard, sprinkling the legs of his brown gabardine flying suit, but he felt only the numb throbbing and was so happy he spoke aloud.

"Jesus!" he said. He looked around at the mountains and smiled, saying goodbye to the valley he knew so well, the splintered villages and the dark green guns and trucks. They'll be here forever, he thought, it will never change. But I won't be here, it's not my business any more, and he looked at his right hand dangling above the control stick with the thumb and forefinger held delicately apart, the other fingers resting on the tip of the rubber grip. On the inside of the hand, at the base of the thumb, a ball of stark white material stuck out like a wad of medical cotton; fat from the cushion at the base of his thumb. It nauseated him to look at it and he wanted to push it back into the flesh, to keep it from the oily cockpit air.

He moved his left hand from the throttle knob and looked at it. Dirty; in the fine cracks of the skin he saw grease and dirt, and the rims of the nails were black. He lifted it to his nose and sniffed: it smelled of gasoline and hot sweat. He put the forefinger in his mouth then rubbed it on the warm gabardine of his chest, cleaning it. Carefully, his left arm swaying with the easy lift and fall of the airplane, he pushed the cleaned finger against the ball of white gristle which sprouted from the base of the right thumb.

Agony crackled along his nerves at once, like a charge of electricity, and he jerked the forefinger away, bending over the control stick with pain. His eyes went glassy and he looked through the propeller blur into glittering, unfocused sunlight, dizzy and unable to find the mountains.

"Oh," he said. He swung his head, blinking, feeling that he was sliding, that one wing tip was going down into a slip and that the airplane's nose was rising higher and higher above the horizon. Then his eyes cleared and the vertigo passed; the mountains appeared again, blue in the haze of altitude. He pushed at the throttle knob, but it was already all the way forward.

He wanted to move, to stand bent forward, cradling his torn right hand in his left, to stand first on one foot and then the other, squeezing his muscles against the pain. But the aileron cable rubbed the crown of his cloth flying cap and his knees were jammed against the twelve-gallon gas tank; his feet were pressed against the rudder cables and pedals, and divided by the fire extinguisher. He could move each foot about an inch. Move, move! his nerves urged him, his calves jerked, but he was fitted into the small airplane like a hand in a tight suede glove, trussed by parachute straps and safety belt, walled in by painted linen and smeared plexiglass. He could not move, and for the first time he was outraged by the smallness of his working space. Before it had seemed compact, inviting, and efficient.

"Why the hell," he said. He was furious with someone, the Army, the taxpayers, the designer, the women in slacks and sweaters who had cheerfully glued and wired this box together while they chewed gum and told dirty jokes. The bastards, he thought, and was certain that no one thought of him at all. Frowning, with his mouth open, he looked down at the trucks, tanks, and jeeps hurrying on a thousand errands. He wanted to land at once, but there was no place to land; there was no place flat enough in the valley, or large enough, or uncluttered enough in all of Italy. God, what a stupid, silly, insolent country, and nobody in it cares about me.

Surely I won't make it, he decided. This is too much, you couldn't expect me to get through this. They probably hit something, the elevators or the rudder or the ailerons; the tubing is probably torn like tinfoil, ready to break. He moved the control stick delicately, feeling for danger but not finding any; of course, you wouldn't know about it until it actually snapped. He looked at the jagged hole in the plexiglass and was weak with fear; a small hole was torn in the *cabane* strut near the window, its edges glinting where the paint was gone. It will collapse, the wings will come off, and I'm too low to jump. And if I try to climb . . . I haven't time to climb and anyway, God, anyway, God damn it, when was the parachute packed? A month, three months ago, some time in the winter?

Ah, now, he thought, now you're in it, all those things are catching up, the things you could have done but didn't. He saw a dreadful mental picture of a soggy parachute, creased tightly, refusing to fill and balloon over the cushioning air. How wonderful it would be to see strong, dry silk, to feel it slipping through your hands, as dry as hot sand, powerful, perfectly made into a carefully stitched parachute! Instead he sat on a lump of useless fabric. It was probably mildewed.

They expected me to worry about everything, he thought, hating the men at the barley field. They thought I could look after every damned thing, that's the way they are, that's all. Selfish, selfish, they couldn't even bother to get the chutes repacked. Nobody ever cares a damn about anybody else, that's just the way it is. They wanted me to fly and spot targets and direct the guns and worry about trying to keep clean, about washing my socks sometimes, and write letters and look out for fighters, and for Christ's sakes they couldn't even get the chutes repacked. If I ever get out of this, if everything works out, they can go fry in hell, and he was impatient to face the shiftless ones from corporal to colonel and shame them with their frivolity.

And the pain increased, rising from the hand through the bones of the right arm, nudging brutally through his body. His neck was stiff, as though he had slept in a cold wind; his muscles ached as with flu, and a new pain began below his left knee. It was odd: it shifted from a burning feeling like a scald, to a freezing, exposed sensation like a knife slash. When it felt hot he wanted to pull the leg of the flying suit away from the skin, but when it felt cold it seemed he could feel the movement of air around the knife cut, a draught which made his skin pucker with goose flesh.

He put his left hand on the kneecap, then slid it over the cloth below it. Surprisingly, the gabardine was torn, as though he had skinned his knee on a gravel road. What on earth, he thought, fingering the torn cloth, but he was careful not to press against the shin. He wanted to look at his leg before he put his hand there and it was impossible to look: if he moved his head forward and down it struck the instrument panel. What a box, he thought angrily. You can't even look at yourself in the Goddamned thing, it isn't an airplane it's a bucket, a phone booth. Then his left hand was easing the throttle knob back and the airplane was nosing down as the engine rattle slowed. He was over the barley field, and he was frightened. I'm hurt, he thought, I'm probably hurt pretty bad now and what's going to happen to me?

He cranked the stabilizer back and dragged in toward the field, settling as the engine let him down until the wheels struck and rumbled on the ground. He chopped the throttle back and braked hard, jerking to a stop, then cut the switch. What's going to happen to me, he thought, fumbling at the safety belt with his left hand, holding the right in front of him. I don't like hospitals and what'll happen to all my stuff while I'm gone?

He opened the flimsy door and saw his mechanic walking toward him.

"Hey," the pilot said, not very loudly, and he started shaking as though he had just been in a serious motor car accident. "Help me," he said. "Help me get out of here, damn it," and the mechanic started running.

Then he was sitting on the ground looking at his shin while somebody tied a fat Carlisle bandage over it. Several people were talking at once. It was the hand, they didn't know what to do with the hand. Someone shook sulfa powder over it, like powdered sugar, but they couldn't decide about a bandage.

"Never mind," he said, unable to understand their foolishness. "God damn it, just get me out of here. I don't want to sit here on the ground, you silly bastards, just get me out of here."

His mechanic put a lighted cigarette in his mouth and he thought, well, for Christ's sake, but then he was very grateful, it was the nicest thing anyone had ever done for him. He had never realized the mechanic was such a sensitive man. But still, the germs; there must be an awful lot of germs around here. He could think about the mechanic later, there would be plenty of time to sort it all out and thank everybody, but the main thing was to get going, to get settled in somewhere, anywhere. It was stupid, sitting in the dirt.

"Will you get going?" he asked them, clenching his right wrist with his left hand. "Will you for God's sake get me out of here?"

Finally he was sitting in the jeep and his leg was hurting more than the hand because he had to bend it getting in. It was becoming stiff, he never wanted to bend it again, and the smoke from the cigarette was stinging his eyes. He worked his mouth, trying to spit out the cigarette, but it clung to his lip.

"Oh, Christ," he said, and it was almost a sob. It surprised him, he felt he might begin crying because things were so perverse. With his left hand he took the cigarette and hurled it away, grudging the time thus lost from holding his right wrist. It was important to hold it, holding kept it in check. He sat in the jeep with his head down, looking at his hand, while the others shouted and ran back and forth for a long time. He decided they didn't realize he was badly hurt; they thought it was a cut finger or a smashed fingernail, that he had been doing a little Sunday carpentering. They believed in Mercurochrome and a patent gauze bandage; he didn't, he never could again. Was this a war or not?

"Let's go," he murmured. He never wanted to see any of them again, they were naïve and irresponsible; he had nothing in common with them at all. "Let's go, let's go."

But as soon as the jeep started he remembered something and twisted around in his seat, frightening the driver; the jeep stopped.

"I forgot to turn off the radio," the pilot said. "We'll have to tell them, the batteries will go dead."

The driver looked at him as though all that which had always held them apart had fallen to the ground; the corporal looked into the lieutenant's eyes with sympathy and understanding for the first time in the pilot's memory. He didn't like it at all; the corporal was a stupid man of forty, a truck driver or a bartender who cared for none of the things the pilot had once held dear, and now he looked at the pilot like that.

"It's okay," said the driver. He shifted back into first gear and sent the jeep bucking over the field to the road. "They got batteries, lieutenant."

Never mind, thought the pilot, and he said nothing, but he thought of this easy violation of his privacy as the jeep sped along the road and was unable to excuse it. He recognized it, all right: the familiarity of strangers at a crash on the highway, the sudden unity of the helping hands of strangers, grasping in ready, un- thinking sympathy the bodies of other strangers. Weak sentiment, bubbling like easy tears from the magazines, the motion pictures and the blue-milk Christianity. Tomorrow, he thought, swaying with the jeep's rapid movement, he'd steal your liquor or your money; right now he's enjoying himself, something has happened to liven things up a bit. He can play a role he likes; why not, he's seen it in the movies. He looked at the driver and was satisfied: the corporal's commonplace face was set in heroic, determined lines, he drove efficiently and with dash. He needs a siren and a bell, and Lew Ayres in the back seat, the pilot thought. You cheap bastard, am I over here for you? It was a bad thing to think: he felt swindled and bullied. He looked at his hand with tears in his eyes, disgusted because he had not seen the vicious joke in time.

The aid station was in a tent, and although the sides were rolled up it was hot under the canvas. It was crowded with soldiers who stood in groups or sat on the ground, men in dirty, ragged clothing who filled the tent with a cheerful buzz of talk. The pilot stood inside the entrance, thinking this could not be the aid station, and then in the crowd he saw islands of medical equipment, trunks which were opened into cabinets, and metal tables. An officer with a stethoscope dangling from his neck moved calmly through the crowd.

The tent was filled with infantrymen; the pilot had never seen them like this, only resting in the villages, shaved and waiting. They laughed loudly now, they offered cigarettes to each other and smiled when a doctor or a medical aid man passed among them. Some of them lay on stretchers, covered with blankets in spite of the heat; most of these had their eyes closed, although one, lying on his stomach, smoked and laughed like the rest, supporting himself on his elbows. Gradually the pilot saw that all were marked with blood on their skins or clothing; some were bandaged, but the bandages were so darkened by blood and dirt they were almost lost against the rumpled uniforms. The pilot hesitated, startled by the happy air of the tent, and the soldiers near him looked up and smiled.

"An Air Corps guy," one of them said, and they looked at the pilot's zippered flying suit.

"No," he said. "Artillery." He didn't want them to think he was from the far away Air Force; it would be an unpleasant note in this happy place, and he wanted to share in their ease and confidence. He looked back to be certain the driver had not left him.

"Wait for me," he said to the driver. "Maybe it isn't so bad," and then a sergeant took his arm and led him through the crowd, out of that tent and into another. The space in between was roofed with a sheet of canvas, he noticed; everything was neatly done here. He hoped the driver would wait for him, however; perhaps it could be fixed here and they would let him go back to his own tent, which was very sloppy, and he could stay on his cot until everything was all right. The cot was rickety and the canvas was split, but he had slept on that cot in that tent for a long time; everything he owned was piled around the cot. He could get somebody to sew up the split.

The second tent wasn't crowded and he felt conspicuous in it. He looked at the doctor and the sergeant and felt he was being melodramatic, standing there with the blood on him.

"I'm sorry to be so much trouble," he said, and regretted it at once. How ridiculous! The doctor smiled, and took his right hand in both of his, looking at it. The sergeant pushed his left sleeve above the elbow and stuck his forearm with a needle.

"What's that?" he said. He looked at the sergeant, than at the doctor. "Will it hurt?"

"It's all right," the sergeant said, and he smiled as the doctor had smiled. Obviously neither of them was paying any attention to what he said, and he felt a little better.

Then they had him lie on a table while they looked at his leg. He craned his neck: more powder was sprinkled on the leg and then on his hand, and this time they bandaged the hand with gauze. He looked at it when they were finished and decided it was a careless job. It was too loose. Still, he was in expert hands now, they knew about the germs, no doubt about that. He felt better and better; when they lifted him to a stretcher he laughed. That wasn't necessary, he told them, but they smiled and carried him into the other tent.

The driver bent down and asked how he felt.

"Fine," he said, smiling at the driver. "It isn't so bad, I guess," but he wished the man would go away. He was eager to join the happy chatter of the infantrymen. The driver wasn't wounded, they didn't want him here. "Come back tomorrow and check again," he told him. "Maybe they'll be through with me, or you can bring my stuff, it isn't far." He was about to add, "You have nothing else to do," but suddenly it seemed too obvious.

The driver went away and he lay under his blanket, cozy as could be; he wasn't cold, but the blanket felt just right. And he was so happy now! He was grateful for everything, the new blanket and the taut ceiling of the tent and the new bandages, and especially grateful for the infantrymen, the wounded. His heart swelled for these gay, battered men; with pity and admiration he thought of the agonies they had endured on the mountains or in the deadly valley, and now here he was, one of them. He could hear them talking in friendly voices and he felt they shared something withheld from the rest of the world. Now they shared it with him.

He was pleasantly tired, as though he had just finished mowing the lawn or playing eighteen holes of golf on a hot afternoon, a little stiff and sore all over but it was all right since he didn't have to move. The blanket really was just right; it was smart of them to know that. And he was surrounded by trustworthy men, the best anywhere; they had suffered and now they knew everything and they knew each other. No matter where he went from now on, no matter what happened, he would always be a part of these men, the honest, the smiling volunteers. It was no longer necessary to grin.

Really, he thought, lying on the hard stretcher which felt so soft and yielding, it's what I've always been looking for and never found before, it's what I always expected from church. He felt a little dizzy, almost drunk, as though he had been drinking beer in the sun; the pain was no more than an ache, just beyond his reach. The afternoon was mild and safe and comfortable; he believed he would sleep before he talked to the infantrymen.

He woke with a grunt and put his hands down to hold the sides of his cot. Pain flared from his right hand as he grasped the wooden edge of the stretcher and then he remembered, and felt he was moving. He opened his eyes as the stretcher was carried out of the tent and the sun burned into his face, blinding him; his eyes watered and the light went out of focus as it had in the airplane. He closed his eyes but the sun still burned painfully through the lids; he was about to say something about it when the sun went away, a gritty shudder ran through the stretcher frame and he felt he was closed up in something. He smelled hot metal and gasoline and realized he was in an ambulance. They had slid his stretcher into a rack and slammed the doors, like a roast going into an oven.

He didn't like it. He opened his eyes and wanted to call out, but he sensed other men in this dim place, and said nothing. A few inches above his face the canvas of another stretcher bulged alarmingly; surely at any minute it would split like his cot and the man above would crash down. Thinking of it made him tense and that hurt; he moaned, and someone else in the ambulance sighed. The sigh startled the pilot; he caught his breath and listened. He missed the laughing infantrymen; something had gone wrong, somehow.

The ambulance began to move, slowly but roughly, and there were more sighs, and more moans. My God, the pilot thought, we'll all be thrown out on the floor. They would be tangled on the steel floor, not knowing each other's wounds, doing terrible damage as they breathed in each other's faces, fighting to get free. With his left hand the pilot held the stretcher bar as hard as he could. The ambulance's silent passengers frightened him; he was too aware that he had lost all control of matters now, that he no longer had any choice in washing his socks or driving over the countryside looking for wine and eggs. He rode blindly in the ambulance and it seemed a long time since he had commanded himself; as he thought about it he was amazed at the freedom he had enjoyed such a short time before, while he was still in the airplane. He kept a tight grip on the stretcher bar and stared at the strained canvas overhead.

The sun was still up when they arrived at the evacuation hospital. It was a group of long tents like those used as cook tents with a circus. As he was carried from the ambulance the pilot recognized the place and was surprised they had not traveled farther. He had often passed the hospital in the jeep, roaming the countryside when he was not flying. It wasn't far from the barley field, perhaps only fifteen miles, but he wasn't certain whether that was good or bad. It was still in his own territory, but surely his hand was more important than this? If I had to go in an ambulance, he thought, if it's that bad.

They carried him into a tent and put the stretcher down at the end of a row of stretchers filled with men. It was like the aid station, but noisier, and bigger, and busier. A girl in green coveralls bent over him and looked at a paper tag which was tied to the zipper pull at the neck of his flying suit.

"How are you, boy?" the girl said, looking at the tag. She had bright red hair and good teeth.

"Fine," he started to say, but she was gone. A southern girl, he decided. The way she said boy. What the hell is this, anyway?

Don't they want to know? Maybe it's on the tag, and he lifted it with his left hand and squinted down his chest at it. He made out his name, his rank, and the letters, "AF"; there was more, but he couldn't read it. AF, he thought, that Goddamned Air Force. I'm sick of the Goddamned Air Force.

"Well when I felt it running down my leg into my shoe I figured it was blood you know, a big vein or something, and it scared hell out of me all right. I remember I figured it must've been a slug that flattened out on a rock before it hit me and I thought Jesus! I just lay there on my gut, scared to move."

The voice came from the ground by the pilot's head. He looked and saw a man lying on his stomach on the next stretcher, an infantry lieutenant with a faded First Rangers patch on his sleeve. He was supporting himself on his elbows, and in his hands he held a silver object with hundreds of tiny silver spears jutting from it. The pilot was reminded of a sunburst frame around an old mirror; the rays in the metal seemed numberless, the object bristled like an angry silver porcupine in the lieutenant's hands, shining in the gloom of the tent. The pilot saw it had been an aluminum water canteen and he listened as the Rangers officer talked to the infantrymen around his stretcher, telling of the explosion of the canteen when the bullet struck it and of the cascade of water which had run down his leg. It all sounded familiar; had he heard the same story at the aid station and forgotten it, or was this one of the war stories you always heard?

"I got some pieces in the butt, just in the cheeks, I think," the Ranger said. "Did you ever hear of anything like that? It don't hurt at all. Did you ever hear of anything so screwy?"

"The purple heart and the red ass, lieutenant," said one of the others, and they all laughed.

These people were just as happy as those at the aid station, but it was beginning to annoy the pilot. He closed his eyes and thought about the canteen, not quite able to believe it. The laughing and joking jarred on him; he felt like hell, he decided. The pain was growing steadily and they all kept laughing, calling out to each other, asking questions, greeting new arrivals.

What the hell, the pilot thought bitterly, they all know each other, it's like a locker room after a game. Is it going to be like that all of my life? For God's sake, is it my fault? I should never have learned to read, I suppose, or anyway not so much. Too much but not enough, that's me. I really knew it all along. The whole world is full of football players. I knew that, too. Damn it, anyway!

He tried to be patient. He lay on the stretcher, waiting, the pain making him nervous and irritable. He no longer had to hold himself against it, however; it burned and ached at a steady level, seeming to get worse because it just stayed there, neither rising nor falling. He could live with it. Hours passed slowly while men were taken out of one end of the tent and others were brought in the way the pilot had come. The men around him discussed their wounds, they repeated again and again the story of what had happened to them on the mountain or in the valley, they greeted new arrivals with jokes and questions. The pilot lost interest in everything that was going on, but the story of an attack was told and retold, and he heard it all, and discovered that most of the men were Rangers. The lieutenant with the splintered canteen gradually dropped out of the conversation; he began to consider himself with alarm and to sink into his problem, the pilot noticed. The morphine drained away in the earlier arrivals and they became morose and complaining, but the newer men maintained the high, nervous chatter.

And then it was the pilot's turn. They carried him into the X-ray tent, photographed his hand, and then left him on the ground. That was all right; the abruptness of the move had frightened him, he wasn't ready for the operating business. Now he concentrated, getting ready for it, but before he was really ready they were back and this time they took him into another tent and slid the stretcher onto a table, under glaring, complicated lights which made his eyes water.

He looked down the tent at the other tables, each occupied by a prone figure and surrounded by a small group of people in white, masked and not to be denied. Someone lifted him by the shoulders and slid a board under his shoulder blades, and when he lay back his arms were extended on the board and strapped down. It was terrible. It was done so swiftly, without a word to him, and now he was helpless. Ah, can't they wait a minute? He looked at the faces above him, trying to look into someone's eyes, but he saw nothing but the white surgical gowns and masks, the intolerable lights and the dark brown rubber gloves of surgery, stern with authority. He swallowed hard, several times: he was frightened and thirsty, and there were tears in his throat.

He kept telling himself these people were here to help him, but it was hard to believe.

"Start counting backward from twenty-five," a woman said, and he felt the swift stab of a needle in the soft flesh of his left arm. He looked at the syringe, wanting it removed; my God, the size of it. . . .

"Twenty-five," he said, trying to say it confidently, "twenty-four, twenty-three, twenty-two, twenty-one, twenty. . . ." and the table slid upward, tilted, and began spinning, a cold wind blew through his intestines and he wanted to sit up before he vomited.

It was eight o'clock in the morning when he awakened and he felt perfectly calm. He looked at his watch and wasn't too surprised that he had slept so long, because he was aware of everything as soon as he opened his eyes and it seemed natural that he had been unconscious or asleep for more than twelve hours. He was lying on his back with his right arm above his head and it tingled, so he moved it and understood at once the strange heaviness of it. A plaster cast covered his hand and forearm. It was a neat, finished job.

Well, he thought, that's the way to get things done. I don't even have a hangover from the dope. He was lying on a cot, fully dressed except for his shoes and somehow he knew they were under the cot. Everything was fine, his left leg was stiff and sore but he was certain it wasn't serious. Well, now this was more like it.

"Good morning," said a voice, and the pilot nodded at the occupant of the cot across from his. There were two rows of cots in the tent with a little open space running between them from one end of the tent to the other. The pilot looked across this aisle at the man who said good morning. He was an infantry captain, a big man with a large head and thick neck. He was sitting up in bed, leaning back against a full barracks bag, with a cigar clenched between his teeth. He worked his thick lips as he spoke but didn't remove the cigar, and this exaggerated his accent, which was either East Texas or Arkansas; for some reason the pilot decided the captain insisted upon and received certain privileges in this tent; was it the cigar?

"You really been knockin' it off," the captain said. He flipped the pages of a flimsy, overseas edition of a news magazine in his lap, then threw it, fluttering wildly, down the aisle. "Damn thing's six weeks old," he said.

"You mean I was snoring?" the pilot asked, not believing it; he was certain he didn't snore.

"Like a P-38," said the captain. He worked his lips around the cigar and frowned in disgust. "When a man cain't even get aholt of a good *se*gar," he said, and he raised his voice to a bellowing tremolo, "When us old bare-assed *he*roes cain't even get a good *se*gar," he roared down the aisle, his voice quivering with mock self-pity, but protesting shouts cut him off, and the pilot was reminded of a college dormitory when the outstanding drunk comes home.

"All right, men," the captain said. "Rest. It's 1943, citizens, and every man jack will be home for Christmas. Ah puhsonally guarantee it. Just keep those V-mails flyin', that's all."

"Keep 'em flyin'!" cried someone at the other end of the tent, making the slogan a jeer.

"Now, wait a minute," said the captain. He looked down the tent reprovingly. "Don't talk dirty like that, we gotta Air Corps fella in here."

"No," said the pilot. "Artillery."

"Well, by granny's crack," said the captain, raising his thick eyebrows. "One of them junior daredevils thrashin' around in a Maytag. We seen you was all zippered up and we figured you was a peashooter," and he raised his voice again. "At ease, men!" he rumbled. "It's Willie the peeper. Youah wives are safe, Ah puhsonally guarantee it."

Several men turned to look at the pilot, smiled at him, and went back to their letter-writing or games of solitaire or poker.

"If Ah'd seen you with your hat on Ah'da knowed anyway," the captain said, and he reached under his cot for another magazine.

The wounded, the pilot thought. Is he one of the wounded? Isn't there more to it than this?

A ward boy brought him his breakfast: a canteen cup of coffee and a metal dish of powdered eggs. It was awkward, eating with his left hand, and he hadn't quite finished the eggs when several ward boys and nurses entered the tent.

The men were carrying a wooden trestle which they placed near him. The plank surface of the trestle was inclined like a ramp, and he saw the boards were splotched with dark stains which had sunk into the grain of the wood. Before he could decide what the trestle meant, a stretcher was brought in and the man on it was lifted onto the trestle; the pilot then realized the trestle was a crude copy of a real hospital bed, almost chest high, but without mattress or springs.

The man on the trestle was unconscious. From his chin to

below his hips he was encased in a plaster cast and at first glance he appeared armless. The pilot was shocked, but then he noticed the abnormal broadness of the man's chest and decided the arms were hidden under the plaster, pressed against the sides of the body. For a minute or so the unconscious man lay uncovered on the boards, his bare legs stretched out below the plaster, white and vulnerable; then a nurse threw a blanket over him and the legs were hidden.

The presence of the man on the trestle subdued the others in the tent. They lowered their voices, the card games slackened in intensity, and although the captain allowed his cigar to go dead several times he said nothing about it but continued to thumb through his news magazines, chewing on the cold cigar and glancing often at the man on the trestle. The pilot, who had awakened ready to begin his role as a wounded man, was both awed and annoyed. He received only the most casual attention during the day and when his hand began to pain him about four o'clock in the afternoon he was grudgingly given two white pills which looked like aspirin. They treat me like a stranger, he thought, and he didn't want to be a stranger; he hadn't come here for that. He hadn't wanted to come here at all, of course, but he was here now and surely he had some rights?

I don't consider myself a hero, the pilot told himself, but after all, it doesn't happen to everybody. These people were different, they'd never even been at the line, and there was no doubt about it, the ward boys and the nurses were not his equals. They should be more courteous and considerate, but he didn't want them to behave like the jeep driver, that moron. I was against all this in the first place, that's it, and now it's been done to me, he told the ward boys and nurses in his mind; that makes it even worse. I don't know what I wanted instead, it gets so you can't even think straight, but it certainly won't settle anything, we don't know what we're doing, but I'm ready to forget all that. You can't get away from it, thought the pilot, I've been wounded, after all; the rest of it doesn't make the slightest difference any more. It doesn't matter when they could have stopped it or why they didn't stop it. It's too late now. That doesn't interest me now. The hell with ideas, you can see how silly they are when something like this happens. There's nothing worse than ideas, in fact, when you get right down to it; they're a blind, they just stick your head in a sack and keep it there until somebody comes along and puts a bullet in your butt. All the ideas that ever were won't change that. What a swindle it all is! The pain increased under the plaster cast and the pilot cursed it, wanting the cast removed so he could reach the pain somehow; he felt that touching it would make it better.

The man on the trestle began moaning about five o'clock. At first the others in the tent pitied him, but as the terrible sounds continued they became embarrassed by so much pain. A doctor came but it was obvious he could do nothing; he looked at the man and spoke to the nurses and the red-haired girl stuck a hypodermic needle into the moaning man's neck. It had no effect; the sounds continued with awful regularity and seemed to grow louder. Strange ward boys and nurses looked into the tent; apparently such moans were not the usual thing, the pilot decided. The red-haired nurse came back, walking briskly; she looked angry. She stood by the trestle and bent forward, looking at the moaning man's closed eyes.

"You quit that now, you hear?" she said loudly, making the pilot jump, but the man on the trestle gave no sign that he heard. "You'll just hurt yourself," the nurse said, and she sounded angry. "Don't be such a baby, now, you hear?"

My God, thought the pilot.

"You'll just wear yourself out, now," said the nurse, glaring at the man's face, but his eyes remained closed.

Jesus, thought the pilot, that's the most horrible thing I ever heard of; perspiration broke out over his body and he longed with all his mind for the nurse to go away, for her to stop bothering the man on the trestle. You silly bitch, he thought, can't you see him?

The moans continued, shuddering, gruesome; the nurse's words failed to interrupt them and she finally left the tent. The man on the trestle was beyond her words, he was beyond everyone in the tent, the pilot thought. It was incredible how far away he was, and yet the moans were the most immediate, unbearable sounds the pilot had ever heard. Their rawness was terrible; the pilot was shocked and frightened by such naked intimacy, he felt that nothing in his entire life had in any way prepared him for this and it seemed outrageous he had never even had a hint about it.

"God damn!" said one of the men in the line of cots, and someone else laughed and then sighed. The pilot felt the muscles around his mouth pull his lips into a grin: it sickened him, but he too wanted to laugh.

"Shut up!" yelled a voice from the cots, a strained, anonymous voice, and again someone laughed quickly.

Yes, thought the pilot, gritting his teeth, shut up, shut up, Jesus Christ, shut up. But the moans kept on, hideously loud.

The red-haired girl and another nurse came into the tent and stood by the trestle, looking at the man's damp, slack face.

"Listen, sugar," said the redhead, bending forward over the man on the trestle. "Can you hear me? I want you to stop that, now, or you'll hemorrhage. You want to make the doctor mad?"

Sugar, thought the pilot, do you want to make the doctor mad; I've got to get out of here.

"Listen, honey," said the redhead. "You've got to stop that. We can't help you if you don't stop," but the man on the trestle kept breathing and moaning. His face was relaxed, his mouth open; it seemed the great moans came from him with no effort whatever since the cast hid the rise and fall of his chest, and this appearance of relaxation made the sounds much worse to the pilot.

"Oh, hell, he's started," the redhead said. She and the other nurse ran out of the tent and the pilot, looking at the man on the trestle, saw a red stain the size of a hand on the plaster over his stomach. As he looked at it it grew slowly, like a drop of red ink on a blotter, and when the nurses came back with the doctors it was no longer a stain: it was wet.

If only I believed in God, the pilot thought, or if only I understood everything that isn't God; one or the other.

The doctors and nurses huddled around the trestle and worked; it was impossible to see what they were doing and the others in the tent made no attempt to see what was being done.

After a time the moans ceased and there was a rustle of relief in the tent, but in a minute or two the man on the trestle began a wet, thick gargling which increased rapidly in tempo with his breathing and then stopped. The pilot knew he was dead, but he didn't believe it; the trestle was removed and a ward boy brought cups of orange juice to the men in the cots and then stood at the end of the tent to see that they drank it, since it was prescribed by the doctors.

What am I like, the pilot wondered, cradling the canteen cup with his left hand and blowing on the orange juice as though it were coffee. I used to read a lot and then I spent a lot of time looking in mirrors when I didn't have anything else to do, making faces at myself, didn't I? I haven't seen a mirror for a long time; now I don't even shave very often and when I do I don't need a mirror any more.

"I'm glad that's over," said the captain. He lighted a fresh cigar and glared at the place where the trestle had been; it seemed to the pilot that the captain was trying to decide what to say; he waited.

"He was the *noisiest* bugger," the captain said, and the pilot let out the breath he had been holding. Still, the captain seemed dissatisfied; he continued to stare in the direction of the vanished trestle, his news magazine neglected in his lap.

Of course, thought the pilot, we don't even know who he was, I didn't even get a good look at his face; it could hardly be anyone I knew. Why worry about it? I've often thought of getting hit, even of dying, you can't help thinking about it; it's like being afraid you'll lose your job. Still, like this, so noisy, and my damned hand hurts so; I'm probably crippled for life. The people back at the field are stupid, but this is worse; what happened to the way I felt at the aid station? Where did all those people go?

The redhead came into the tent. She stopped at several cots and finally reached the pilot.

"You're going for a ride, boy," she said, copying his name from the tag on his zipper pull into a book.

"Where?" asked the pilot; he wasn't quite ready to think of moving.

"Africa," said the redhead, closing the book. "By air, first thing in the morning. Now hit the sack, you've got a full day to-morrow."

Oh, no, thought the pilot, but the redhead was gone. Back to Africa, where the whole thing started? He was dismayed at the thought of it, it seemed to undo all the months of war since he had left Africa; he was surprised that anyone was in Africa at all. More than anything else he wanted to go back to his tent and his cot; he would lie there until he was well, why couldn't they let him do that?

The mechanic is stupid, the driver's a moron, he thought, but at least we're accustomed to each other. How terrible to be among strangers from now on; he didn't think he could do it and he saw with maddening clarity what it would be like in Africa, in the backwash of war: the hospital in a colonial barracks like a prison; the thieving ward boys grown soft and easy; the awkward, un-attractive nurses as regimented as those at home, jumpy with urges that somehow were never fulfilled, so far from the battle they were no longer even moved by pity; and the doctors, slowly becoming brutalized by boredom, their work done for them in Italy, taking temperatures and feeling pulses, keeping records, inspecting the beds, no longer excited, spending hours at the beach, where they drank too much and sat looking out at the empty sea. The war, the world gone elsewhere; there was nothing to do on the hard edge of Africa.

I'll have to come back as quickly as I can, thought the pilot, and he stirred restlessly on his cot, ready to begin the coming back at once, but then he realized there was nothing to come back to, no one to come back to as there had never been, and the impatience left him as suddenly as it had come. He was not impatient and he felt no pity for the man on the trestle nor, inexplicably, for himself. He disdained pity and impatience in an instant, after living with them for an age and it was a strange, wonderful sensation, as pleasant as morphine: in his mind he saw the billowing, cresting cumulus clouds which hung always over the valley in the north, powerful, solid clouds as mighty as mountains but as light as new bandages, the clouds which always fascinated him because he could never be certain they were empty. And to the pilot, calmed and slowed now in his new disdain, it seemed the clouds explained something to him, he hardly knew what: he thought of their loveliness and of the stinging fighters which sometimes came from their blue and white clefts, of the clouds, towering over the valley and the mountains, and he told himself, I'm ready now, and went to sleep.

And outside of the tent, in the Italian night, where no lights shone that year save the stars and moon, the pineboard skeleton of the trestle crouched with its head lifted rigidly into the wind that blew from the valley in the north.

the bankrupt

⁑ Certainly he was the vainest man I've ever known: if he had lived I'm sure he would have made many people unhappy but somehow, from the very first, I felt he wouldn't live. Or so it seems now. At the time I probably didn't think about it one way or the other, since I wanted to live myself and that took up most of your time, just thinking about it.

But this vanity of his: it really was inexplicable. His face was that of a petty thief: you could hardly remember it for five minutes. His uniform was always sloppy, his stomach bulging over his belt, the belt buckle dull, his leggings not laced tightly enough. The seat of his fatigues bagged, his overseas cap kept the manufacturer's wrinkle and his shoes were rarely shined. And yet, one of his little sidelines was a business he carried on with the post cleaning and tailoring shop as a commission man. The uniforms never fitted, of course, and to get them fixed you took them to Liebknecht. He could also bring back from town brass insignia and belt buckles for those who couldn't leave the post for some reason or other, and, since soldiers take delight in these little things, the only means they have of dressing themselves up, Liebknecht did a fat business in crossed cannons, U.S. buttons, battalion insignia and garrison caps with stiff wire grommets in them. The brass objects were always plated: the brass wore off under the Blitz cloth, and the recruits were told that garrison caps were not permitted in armored units, but Liebknecht had his profit. The brass cannon and buttons were thrown away when the tin showed through, and the garrison caps went into barracks bags, to be worn on furloughs which never came. I think Liebknecht even sold Air Force wings to some soldiers for furlough use: an armored artillery battalion did not seem very glamorous at home.

Liebknecht's commercial success fed his vanity, no doubt: his appearance could not have sustained it. He bragged and boasted of how much he made, talking rapidly in a slum accent, overriding everyone who tried to interrupt, turning his head from one to another of us, his eyes flat and lifeless no matter how excited his voice became.

"Why be a sucker?" he would say, sitting on somebody's cot, leaning forward, talking above the noise of the small-time latrine crap game. "I ain't going to be in this Army all my life, am I?"

We did not know. We could not answer him, and after waiting for his answer he would grin and snort, massaging his rubbery, boneless nose with the back of his pudgy hand.

"I had an uncle in the last war," he would say, until somehow we conceived a terrible idea of the last war, of hordes of Liebknechts in mustard-brown stiff uniforms, swarming over the battlefields in search of trades, of profits, of little sidelines on the banks of the Marne. "He was a Marine," Liebknecht would say, and we would think of Chateau Thierry and the Marines swarming and trading and grinning there, Liebknechts all, although we knew his uncle had never left the States. It was something the Liebknechts were proud of, our Liebknecht told us: "He cleaned up," he said. "He made thirty g's in a crap game lasted four days. In Brooklyn navy yard," and our Liebknecht would curse because he was in Oklahoma.

Well, we did not know. We were not sure. We took our

tailoring to Liebknecht and watched his profits grow. If you did not give him your business you had to carry your clothes clear into town on the bus, and you might not get back for a month to pick them up. Or you might never get back: we could go overseas at any time, they said. Besides, Liebknecht was a friend of the first sergeant: it did not pay to ignore a friend of the first sergeant. When we got overseas, of course, it would be a different matter: at least twelve men had sworn to kill the sergeant on the first dark night abroad, and two hard cases made knives from files in the motor pool shop for that very purpose.

Nobody said so, but the implication was that once overseas we would do with our tailoring as we wished. Actually, as with Liebknecht himself, it was something we were not sure about: we did not know if one worried about tailoring and cleaning and pressing overseas, but we had a vague premonition about it: we wanted no specific information. We knew in our hearts it was a terrible thing to be burdened like that with the thought of clothes, to have them forever on our minds, but there it was, nothing to be done about it. We were well trained, after all. We were not stupid, exactly: we knew some of us were certainly going to die but there was a terrible gap in our knowledge: we did not know which were going to die and which were not, and so we all had to keep on worrying about such things as our clothes. We wanted to look nice, I guess: we were extremely well trained.

The great day came at last, of course: encumbered and cluttered and weighted until our knees trembled with the stiff equipment of war, we boarded a troop train: for New York, Liebknecht said. We carried packs of blankets rolled in canvas tent halves, shovels, picks, rifles, pistols, submachine guns, barracks bags; intricate patterns of webbed belts crossed and crisscrossed our bodies until we could hardly move and we peered out, frightened and stunned, from under the unaccustomed weight of steel helmets. Liebknecht boarded the train too, his sole equipment a clipboard which he carried in his hand: his gear was already in the kitchen car, he said. He seemed to check off names from a list, and when darkness came he went up and down the aisles selling nickel candy bars for twenty-five cents. We bought them eagerly, because we were leaving the known for the unknown, I suppose: there was no liquor and so the candy helped. Well, now, we thought, this is the way you begin to die, maybe, and we sat under the blue lights of the wartime troop train, eating candy bars and trying to accustom ourselves to this enormous commonplace. It wasn't easy, and before the trip was over Liebknecht sold out his stock.

I remember two things about that night very clearly: a crap game started in the vestibule of our car and when I passed it on my way to the toilet I noticed one of the players had a roll of green toilet paper behind him and was tearing off sheets of it and covering the bets of the others: he was safe under the blue lights except when we passed a station or when somebody like me came by with a flashlight. The other thing I remember was Liebknecht, swaying with the rapid motion of the train going through the night, murmuring as he stopped at each seat: "Any you guys want candy bars?" and he would shake the box, rattling the candy bars in their stiff wrappers. We ate too many and suffered from thirst, because the water coolers broke down as soon as the train started.

In the embarkation camp on the banks of the Hudson Liebknecht sold whiskey. It was improbable, even impossible, but he had it, at ten dollars a pint, and he started telling us he was sending his money home to his mother. Well, we did not know. We were getting very close to salt water and we did not care whether he had a mother or not. Maybe he said he was sending the money to his "old lady." That could have meant anything, but if Liebknecht had had a mother he would have called her his "old lady." We bought his whiskey during the three nights we stayed in that place, and on the last night a fight started in the latrine of B battery's barracks over the question of whether we were going to Hawaii or Iceland.

Liebknecht knew, of course: it was Africa. He threw away the suit of gas-proofed long underwear we were issued that last night and bragged about it later, laughing at us. He was right: the underwear was stiff and clogged with a greasy material which was supposed to keep the gas from burning you, and it rubbed off on everything in our barracks bags. Not only that, but they made us turn it in in Africa. We weren't supposed to have it at all, apparently.

We did not see Liebknecht when we boarded the train for the trip to the ship. We staggered, more heavily laden than before by new issues of equipment, and spent a humiliating hour standing in a railway station next to the bay, waiting for a ferry. An Italian boy in my section wet his pants, and when we heard the sergeant's whistle 'way up ahead we all started to run, as though there was a chance we might be left behind.

At the ship's gangway stood Liebknecht, submissively and unobtrusively to one side, out of the way of the officers, but standing there with his clipboard in one hand and a cup of Red Cross coffee in the other. The Red Cross ladies were smiling and poking paper cups at us but we were carrying so many objects we could not accept, of course: the Italian boy could not even get a hand free to sling his gas mask carrier around so it would cover his disgrace, but the Red Cross ladies pretended not to notice. They were used to that kind of thing, I guess. As I remember, they all had faintly blue gray hair.

The ship seemed as solid as the land: she swallowed us as calmly and insultingly as though an affair of this magnitude happened every day. The ship was bored: the crew was bored, the naval officers were terribly bored. They could not stand cattle, obviously: they handed out our life belts with a disdain which almost amounted to treason and implacably ordered us below.

The word went out at once that the ship was monstrously, insanely overloaded: someone heard our officers arguing about it with the ship's captain. The Navy said it had been told to expect a certain number of men: instead of that, three times that many were now aboard. In the dim, bad air of the hold, we looked at each other: the steel walls were sweating, the sea rose on all sides, it was dark and hot and equipment was strewn over every inch of deck space: the Red Cross ladies seemed a thousand miles away, instead of twenty feet, and we felt trapped in a mine shaft, watching dumbly as the shaft was sealed up overhead. We were not exactly guilty of anything, we thought: our defenselessness only made it appear that way. There was no mistaking it now: somehow, we had been careless, we had given up a part of ourselves to irresponsible persons who were now claiming the whole, we had kept on laughing just a bit too long. And into this scene walked Liebknecht, with some news: his cousin was the ship's storekeeper. We looked at him standing in the little shaft of light which came down the stairs, and the ship sailed.

A third of the men were seasick before we passed Staten Island; the toilets overflowed at Ambrose Light, to remain out of order for fifteen days; the wash water was salt and so would not lather our soap, although we had to shave every day; we slept and ate in three shifts, so that breakfast for some fell at four in the afternoon, for others at midnight, with lunch at six in the morning; the officers feared we would throw away our overcoats when we learned we were going to Africa, and so required us to carry them with us all day long in the summer weather and to toil downward into the depths of the ship with them, wearing them in the chow lines where steam swathed us from the stoves and men fainted, vomiting from the heat, and after ten days of cloudless weather we were ordered to bring all our equipment up from the holds and spread it on deck for inspection, whereupon a storm hurried over the horizon and soaked our belongings, while we were below making a clean sweepdown fore and aft. It was hilarious and it was hell, and Liebknecht bunked with his cousin among the pampered crew. He began to sell us salt-water soap and good razor blades and cigarettes, instead of the cheap issue variety; his candy-bar stock was wonderfully replenished and now each bar was worth a dollar. And we paid his price, we argued for a chance to pay it, we shoved and insulted each other, sugar-starved and frightened, the children of the soft drink and the ice cream parlor and the beer joint: deprived of sweets and alcohol and certainty, we begged Liebknecht to take our dollars. Where we were going we could not use money, we believed: if the enemy didn't get us the Arabs would, because that was what the Book said.

The Book was horror in paper covers, a catalogue of warnings and threats called "Soldier's Handbook: North Africa." Its purpose was to make Morocco and Algeria into outskirts of hell. Each sentence began, "It is forbidden." It was forbidden to look at an Arab woman, even if she had on a veil, the Book said; it was forbidden to ask Arabs for alcoholic beverages, because their religion forbade such stuff; it was even better not to speak to them at all, the Book said, as they did not like infidels: all they liked was to emasculate people they didn't like, and we began to wonder if the war should not be carried on by the WAC's, or the Army Nurses Corps. It was forbidden to eat any fruit or vegetables in North Africa, the Book said, since all crops were fertilized with human offal: still, we could not get very excited over that, since we didn't see how we could live long enough to find any fruit or vegetables. There were scorpions everywhere, and no water supply was safe. The Book was not certain, but probably poisonous snakes abounded in some areas. All this was serious enough, but the book tactfully ignored the worst aspect of Africa: the Afrika Korps. Possibly we had an early edition, but in any case we knew we weren't going to need money. Candy bars shot up in price as the convoy neared Gibraltar and the destroyers started chasing submarines. Liebknecht announced he had given his money to the battery commander to keep for him: the sum was now so large, he hinted, that he felt it unsafe to keep it himself. The risk was too great. However, he discounted the statements made in the Book: there was sure to be some little business or other to be carried on in Africa, he said, and his attention wandered when we mentioned the Afrika Korps.

In Oran we saw he was probably right: Arab prostitutes milled in the dock area, unveiled, painted and mascaraed: they shouted, "Hey, soldier, me pink inside like Queen Victoria!" forty years behind the times but unmistakably not forbidden. The Arab men smiled upon us, they filled our canteens with green wine for a dollar, they offered to pay twenty dollars for our empty barracks bags or mattress covers. Liebknecht was frenzied: within two days he had a ring of Arabs working with him in our staging area. The price of wine went up to two dollars, barracks bags dropped to ten, all deals handled through Liebknecht. He was becoming, unmistakably, rich. He even sold us the vegetables we were not supposed to eat, and we bought them as we had bought the candy bars, because the heat was relentless and the water a chemical joke: we devoured small, tasteless melons and began to look at Liebknecht with respect. He had not been wrong so far, we said, and began to feel indignant with ourselves. The war wouldn't last forever, we said, and we spoke of making a little something on the side. One man sold a jeep tire and was court-martialed; another was strangled in an Arab bordello. But Liebknecht, impregnable Liebknecht, prospered. He was almost a spiritual leader, if we had any spiritual substance, a figurehead, a billboard, the national dream. He spoke of expensive cars and a speedboat, and smoked good cigars. He was going to own a restaurant and bar in New York. He might give some of us jobs in the kitchen, he said. We listened and grinned, taking it all, watching and trying to understand how he did it, bewitched out of our senses. Bewitched, because we had forgotten something, something which Liebknecht apparently had never known, had apparently never troubled to notice because it did not fit into his insanely rational system, because it was insanity itself made reasonable and huge: the war. The battalion finished staging and headed east along the coast for the front.

We went in a long, roaring convoy under a pall of dust so thick and penetrating it seemed a solid, dust so old and finely powdered on this hard rind of Africa that it coated us like dried clay, turning men into gray lumps which cracked and split when they moved. And Liebknecht too was dusted, coated and choked, at first swearing and then silent, awed or bored by this incredible, absurd column of dust which blocked out the mountains and the sea, the vineyards and the white cubes of Arab houses. We were a holocaust of dust and thousands of tons of metal, roaring blindly up the road all day, the men in each tank or halftrack able to see only the tank or halftrack ahead, and everybody wondering and hoping that the colonel was in front and knew what he was doing, where he was going. When we stopped at last and the dust settled we saw the sun was just down beyond the mountains. We went into our first position there, spread around the outskirts of a deserted village of about ten houses. Headquarters and service batteries found places for themselves in the houses; the gun batteries were further away.

Liebknecht, we now learned, was officially a message center runner for headquarters battery: it was odd, but we had never thought before just what his job was. He produced a sagging brass bedstead from a house, set it up in the house where the cooks were, and before chow was ready was selling PX supplies, Arab souvenirs and pieces of German equipment.

We had finished eating and were standing in line at the wash tubs with our messkits when B battery started firing, over on the left. It was the first time we had seen the guns going in earnest and everybody ran up on a little knoll to watch. It looked very serious: you looked out into the darkness and then suddenly the six M-7's would be lighted up by their big orange muzzle flashes, silhouetting men and jeeps for an instant, then the shock of the explosions and faintly, in the echo, you could hear the rustle of the shells going out and away in the night. It was eerie, and we didn't talk much: I had the feeling that we were going pretty far with this thing; we were likely to get somebody mad, doing anything as irresponsible as this. After all, we didn't even know what the country was like, it struck me, and here we were firing 105-

millimeter shells out there eight or nine thousand yards into the dark. And on top of that the muzzle flashes were so huge I didn't see how we could help being found out. I had thought a lot about what it would be like, but none of this had occurred to me at all. I was embarrassed by our presumptuousness and our racket, and I had a strong desire to pretend I didn't have anything to do with the whole crowd.

The firing went on for about ten minutes and then stopped. We stayed on the knoll, waiting to see if they'd start again but they didn't. It began to get cold, and we were glad we hadn't thrown away our overcoats. After a while we went down to the village and discovered Liebknecht had found some Arabs and was selling wine. We told him about B battery, but he wasn't interested.

"Probably just showing off for some general," he said, and kept filling canteens, at five dollars each. "You guys want to worry about something, find me some of them Kraut rotating bands," he said.

Rotating bands were rings of bright, soft metal which fitted around a shell and were cut by the barrel's grooves when the gun was fired, giving the shell the spin which held it on its course. We had seen souvenir cigarette lighters made from them in Oran, where sailors were paying Arabs ten or fifteen dollars each for the bands, and Liebknecht said he would give us three dollars for any we found. He had a system to get them back to the port, he said. We saw his margin of profit, as usual, but we had no system: we never had one. We lived in a lethal world, armed and armored, but somehow we were unarmed against Liebknecht, who seemed invincible and invulnerable. Still, he was terribly vulnerable, because he did not realize he had changed worlds: if we learned anything, we learned that from our Liebknecht.

We lay down that night in our blankets for the first time "in support," as the army calls artillery at the front, but I don't think anybody went to sleep. B battery began firing again, a single gun adjusting, then the other guns and then A battery and C battery began firing too. You could not have expected so much noise. The house where I was quartered shook and dust sifted down from the walls, and through the place where the door had been I watched the low, rocky hills light up suddenly from the flashes, the scrub trees throwing long, quick shadows in the orange flare, the noise incessant, as though a machine had gone out of control and was shaking itself to pieces. And then the guns stopped, the echoes rolling hugely among the hills, the whisper of the last shells fading quickly out and away, and in the house we shifted under our blankets.

"For Christ's *sake!*" somebody said bitterly and righteously, and somebody else said, "Man, I sure hope they know what they're doing."

The silence lasted perhaps ten minutes, then noise began again, and the hills were lighted in brief flashes. But this time the light was more white than orange, and the noise was different. At first I couldn't tell exactly how the sound had changed. I sat up, leaning on one elbow, listening: mixed in with the explosions were shrill whines and whistles, followed instantly by vicious buzzings, as though maddened bumble bees were driving for my ears. I knew without being told, although we had wondered if perhaps we would not *have* to be told: these were shells bursting in the village, not the sounds of our batteries firing.

Instantly I was indignant with our guns: they had *not* known what they were doing, and now look! It was infuriating, and I was going to say so, but everybody started shouting at once and we knew we were frightened for good now, probably forever.

"Them crazy bastards!" somebody yelled in the darkness near me, yelled it in a voice of fear, helplessness and futile rage: there had been a serious error somewhere, and we all felt it, and were not to blame. That was what was so maddening: we were being made to pay for somebody else's mistake, never our own, we thought, until we began to think that was the story of our lives.

The shelling stopped, of course: we did not count the bursts or the minutes. We lay for a moment in the silence and the darkness, then leaped up and started for the door. But we heard it coming this time, our ears marvelously tuned in such a short time, the peculiar, never-to-be-mistaken sound of the incoming shell, piercing, shrieking, splitting the air from over the horizon to here, now, this instant and this spot quicker than a breath, and we hit the floor as it burst outside.

The fragments buzzed and clanged off the rocks, and in the same noise we heard a shrill sound, and although it did not sound at all like the movies, we knew it was a man screaming. It did not sound any more like a real man than like a man in the movies, but we really did know what it was: it was a terrified sound so inhuman that only a man could make it.

In a few seconds the screaming stopped. We did not hear any more shells coming; moving softly, cautiously, so we could listen to the air, we moved outside. It was Liebknecht, of course: as we tiptoed fearfully over the harsh, rocky ground we heard him gasping, a wet, thick gasping like a ripsaw cutting green wood, and in the gasping he kept saying, "Don't they know?" Just like that, over and over again: "Don't they know? Don't they know?" We weren't sure what he meant.

He had run out of his house to look for rotating bands from the bursting shells. Since he was the first man killed in the battalion they gave him a posthumous Bronze Star and of course he got the Purple Heart automatically. They put on the Bronze Star citation that he had gone out under fire to check the telephone lines, since that would have been his job if he had ever gotten around to going to work. We had to leave him on the ground next to the house under a shelter-half until the next night when a graves registration service truck could come up for him, and they didn't get there until about four in the morning and by that time some damned Arab or other had sneaked in and stolen his clothes. Army clothing was worth quite a lot at that time. The graves registration people put him in a mattress cover service battery had used that morning to bring up bread in. It shocked us, I remember, but we found out later that was the standard way to do it: s.o.p., it was called, standard operating procedure. There were a lot of little trick names and initials for things in those days.

"Then was love so great that each man set his neighbor on high: but now hath love grown cold and the whole world is set in malice, and each doth pull down his neighbor to the lower room, and for this reason we come short of grace."

—FROM *The Desert Fathers,*
translated from the Latin by Helen Waddell

the lower room

[1] That morning the Italian air was filled with distant dust, thin, hanging on horizons and blurring far away outlines as it had all that wartime summer. From the heights the valley floors faded into milky flatness: it was difficult to see accurately beyond the nearest villages. The roads looked like beds of chalk laid open by diggers, white and empty beyond the river.

The highway was not white, but a dirty asphalt blue. It came down the valley out of the north haze as straight as new wire, halted at the river, then continued on the other bank and disappeared into Cassino in a tight, lefthand curve. When the highway came south out of the town it was changed, familiar, pitted and despised. It dipped and rose, bent itself around the hills and straightened, going south a hundred miles across the plain.

South along the highway, as far from the river as a man could move on the ground in a day, for the highway was broken and twisted and the traffic thick, the mouth of a sunken road touched the highway's shoulder. In this road men traveled below the level of the fields as though in a deep, eroded trench which twisted across the countryside. Overhead the sky was a pale, empty blue,

153

its color weakened by the dust which hung high and formless in the air.

The road was so old that no one could remember its name, nor if it had ever had a name. If anyone asked the people who lived near it what it was called they moved their hands quickly but inconclusively, jerking up their hands and spreading the fingers before their chests, opening their mouths several times but saying nothing. Their eyes would widen at the question: they would look at the road and then at the questioner, then back at the road.

"The road!" they would cry. It was the road from the village, and there was no other. "The road! The road!" and they would glare, and shrug, and walk away.

Ten minutes walk from the village the floor of the road rose until the traveler was again in the open, crossing the neat fields toward the first houses, the outpost houses scattered thinly around the base of the rocky hill where the stone buildings of the village jutted up like rocks themselves. Hill and village were a light, streaked gray, their details and outlines blurred by age and weather until each merged with the other in a dead mass. The village lay like a shattered stone, loosely whole, ready to fall apart when struck again by the convict's hammer. Its blank windows looked down on the dry fields and the two monoplanes.

They were small and weak, but their color was a dark, heavy green. They were tethered with ropes to stakes driven into the stubble field, and they rocked and quivered in the hot wind which blew over the plain and might have tumbled away like leaves if the ropes had not held them, for they were only skeletons of aluminum tubing covered with painted linen. A man could lift one by the tail and pull it along behind him.

In heavy, solid contrast with the trembling airplanes, a halftrack stood nearby, plated and squat on its flat caterpillar treads. It anchored the ropes along one side of a green pyramidal tent. The tent was smeared with patches of dried mud and had a worn, sagging look, as though its canvas had been allowed to slacken in wind and sun.

Inside, three men sat on army cots, surrounded and encumbered by a jumble of metal rods, engine parts, coils of wire, aluminum tubing and splintered, useless propellers. They collected such things from wrecked airplanes and were especially fond of instrument panels: each man had one, but could not use it, nor had they any use for the rest of their collection. Still, they were unable to throw it away: they carried it with them wherever they went, loading it into the halftrack with curses and threats against each other. Each man considered his share the most interesting and could not understand the portions of the others, although a visitor from the village could not have told one portion from another.

The slippery heap of a white nylon parachute was piled on the cot of one of the men: he snipped at it with a pair of chromium pinking shears, cutting along the corded seams. Like the others he was dressed in green cotton coveralls with four chevrons on the sleeves. His name was Schultz, and he was the mechanic of the monoplanes.

He was a round-faced man in his late thirties, with a red, rubbery nose and puffy cheeks. A sudden little potbelly sat on his thighs under the coveralls and when he wore trousers he pulled the belt tightly across the belly, trying to disguise it, but only succeeded in making two melons where there had been one. His stomach had a permanent crease in it from this practice and those who saw him naked, his white, damp flesh creased in this way, sometimes pictured the organs inside as squashed and deformed by his vain habit. Schultz was aware of his peculiar-looking stomach but no longer worried about it. It was common among men of his age and habits, he believed. He was about fifteen years older than the other two sergeants, the pilots of the monoplanes, and it was they, more than any others, who had to look at his stomach.

He dropped the parachute, which he was cutting into scarves, took a cigarette from his coveralls and lighted it.

"I knew a girl in Berlin, worked in a parachute factory," he said, and he looked at his cigarette with distaste. "She lived across the hall from me in the second house I lived in. A Latvian, from

Riga. We used to go out together and she'd have to sneak back upstairs with her shoes off."

"Oh, for Christ's sake, Schultz!" cried Moore. He got up from his cot and stood jiggling on first one foot and then the other, his fists clinched and held in front of him in a boxing position.

Schultz smiled and started to speak, but Moore shouted at him.

"I don't care, you know!" he cried. "But the fact is, Schultz, there's a war on, you know! I've heard enough about you and your German friends."

He sat down suddenly, holding his clasped hands tightly between his knees. "I'm the one who has to take it, you know. I'm the one who was always making excuses to the captain for you, telling him you were flying to group, or checking the rigging or breaking in a new engine. If he knew anything about airplanes—anything at all!—you'd both be in the stockade."

The third sergeant, a young man with sleepy eyes, swung his legs over and sat on the edge of his cot.

"Ho!" he said, squirming happily, jiggling his feet up and down. His name was Miller, and Moore was pretty sure he hated him as much as he hated Schultz. "I'll take that, wouldn't you, Schultz? I'll take the stockade, come on, come on, put the cuffs on me," and he held his hands out toward Moore, his wrists together. "Duncan only thirty miles away—"

Moore glared at him for a moment, then stood.

"Miller, I really believe you're a moron," he said. He turned, stooped and left the tent.

Miller and Schultz sat without speaking until they heard Moore's footsteps fade away. Schultz lighted another cigarette and resumed his preoccupied look, ignoring the swaths of nylon which lay around him like an unfinished bridal gown.

Miller hummed a passage from an unrecognizable song, then fell back on his cot.

"Let's have a drink somewhere," he said.

"Call room service," said Schultz, without changing his expression.

"One of these gooks around here will have something," Miller said, staring sleepily at the tent roof. "You're a college man, you can find it."

Schultz frowned. "Don't be a jerk," he said.

"The cup that cheers," Miller said. "Past regrets and future fears, hot damn! What gets into him, anyway?"

Schultz flipped cigarette ashes onto the white nylon.

"He tries too hard," he said. "He's from Texas. How the hell do I know what's the matter with him?"

The hot sun fell on the tent and on the fields, and the mountains quivered in the heat. In the distance they heard a machine gun firing in short practice bursts and the harsh voice of a peasant driving oxen came to them from the road.

"I'm ready to go back up," Schultz said, wiping the sweat from his face with his sleeve. "I'm sick to death of this hole."

"Why, certainly," Miller said angrily. "Why not, why not? All you do is sit on your can at the strip, you can't even cook."

"Just the same," said Schultz. "Just the same. They don't even do your laundry around here the way they should. Besides, I'm not a *flieger*, I ain't the type. That's for you, bright boy."

"Ain't?" said Miller, sitting up and staring at the mechanic. "I thought you were gonna help me with my English."

Schultz sighed and pushed the nylon away from him.

"You're corrupting me," he said, lying down on his cot. "You're a stinking influence, Miller."

Remember now, he told himself, lying down and closing his eyes, remember, there is no such thing as a bad boy.

[11] When Moore left the tent he walked angrily out into the hot field and started toward the river. Then, remembering the streambed was dry, he stopped. The wish to be someplace other than where he was, to be present where something, anything was happening was strong in his brain and body. His fingers were stiff with impatience and anger and he felt he would strike out at

anyone who came near him, a crushing, slamming blow with his fists. A feeling of pleasure swept upward from his stomach as he thought of smashing his knuckles into some still featureless face, kicking savagely at the body as it writhed on the yellow stubble, jumping with both feet on the helpless creature's stomach.

"Unh!" he grunted through clenched teeth, feeling the violence of straining muscles and the burning liquid forming in his stomach. "Unh, unh, unh!"

Suddenly conscious of himself, he looked quickly around to see if he was being watched, then walked over to one of the monoplanes and sat down in the shade of its wing.

He was barely into his twenties and he frowned a great deal, as he did now, as though someone had asked him a complex question which he did not quite understand. "What? What did you say?" his expression asked with wrinkled forehead and worried, deepset eyes, saying that this was important and he wanted to understand it, and he would understand it if only everybody would keep quiet for a minute.

"So hot," he said aloud. Unbottoning his coveralls to the waist, he leaned back against the airplane's balloon tire and stared at the tree line which marked the dry riverbed. Even under the wing the heated air pressed against him like a tank exhaust, and the wing itself seemed to pour out heat from its smooth, painted linen surface. The fabric made small popping sounds as the sun tightened the doped skin of the airplane, stretching it metal-hard over the wooden ribs and braces of the wing's skeleton.

He jerked a piece of stubble out of the dry earth and chewed it, thinking of Miller and Schultz in the tent.

Laughing at me, he thought. But I know they're wrong, it isn't right, that's all. I can't quite get my hands on it, but it isn't right.

Schultz and Miller astonished and enraged him. He had lived a year with them in a tarpaper hut on the dry, barren plains of the fort in Oklahoma as the artillery battalion trained, and he had lived with them on the equally dry and barren land of Africa, on the edge of that continent, as dry and hard as a rind. Now he lived with them in Italy, but only the places had changed. Schultz and Miller remained the same. Even the war did not move them, it seemed. Sergeant Moore thought of the war with fear and enormous respect, and felt he owed it something. Miller, whose job was the same as Moore's, paid hardly any attention to it all, in Moore's opinion. Miller went where the war was and flew above it as he was expected to, but it was perfectly obvious he did not believe those who told him, "That's a war down there." Moore found this annoying but almost understandable, since Miller was a product of institutions: an orphanage, the CCC's, and now the Army. But Schultz! Ah, there was no accounting for Schultz, the scoffer, the criminally wise, who often said the Allies might well lose the war. He was intolerable, but inescapable: he lived in the same tent, he was always on hand to tie down the airplane when Moore landed, he came back from the villages in the nights and urinated drunkenly on the tentpole, while Miller shouted warnings and threats and Moore lay rigid in the darkness, his jaws locked in anger.

Schultz was at his worst during slack periods such as this, when the war seemed to stall. Sitting under the wing in the heat, Moore wished recklessly that a huge attack would come and set them in motion, since the closer Schultz approached to the war, the quieter he became. For weeks now they had sweated, unmoving, in the little plain below the village.

"He'll do something awful soon," Moore murmured, as though by saying this aloud he could drag the fact out in the open and choke it. He wished again, bitterly, since the wish threatened his own life, that the front would cave in. Before the war, before Schultz, such carelessness would never have occurred to him, he knew. In the Texas town where he grew up he had not gone barefooted in the alleys, since he feared broken glass and rusty tin cans, which gave you lockjaw, and in the woods he had never picked up a snake, not even a dead one. When the others flicked at rattlers with sticks, he did so too, but his stick was always longer, and he hung back when the rocks rained on the writhing serpents' heads, and he never picked them up afterward from the creek bank. And now, because of Schultz, he wished himself back in something much worse than the terror of the damp creek bottoms. It was a dreadful notion, and Sergeant Moore sat sweating under the wing, thinking of his room in his parents' house, cool and dim on hot afternoons. He had left it willingly, eagerly, but something had gone fearfully wrong, the world had jammed. Moore knew that if something did not give quickly he would explode, like a badly fused shell dropped at the breech. Schultz, the clumsy cannoneer.

And, deliberately, malignantly making it worse, Schultz knew what he was doing. Did Miller?

"Scum!" said Sergeant Moore suddenly and loudly, and he glared over his shoulder at the tent.

And quoting poetry, in his Illinois twang! Sergeant Moore groaned under the airplane wing, thinking of Miller's delight in rhymes. In the little tin ammunition box which Miller kept under his cot was a pocket edition of *The Oxford Book of English Verse* and every night in the tent he read it by the glow of his flashlight, usually aloud, in spite of Moore's protests. His favorite was "The Ballad of Bouillabaisse" (which he pronounced "bullabase"), and he would repeat it and repeat it until Moore left the tent to stumble around in the dark outside, staying out to listen to the guns rumbling on the horizon until Miller's voice died away and the flashlight was out in the tent. There were ways to behave, Moore thought, and in a war that was not one of them.

[III] In the tent Schultz was so bored he lay absolutely still, refusing to move even his eyelids as Miller rustled in his tin ammunition box, looking for something in the mess of old fruit drops, dirty writing paper, paperbound books and other things he kept there. His fumbling sounded like a puppy wrestling with old newspapers, Schultz decided.

"What we need is a dog," he said to the tent roof, without opening his eyes. "Something to keep us amused."

"No, I want a fiddle," Miller said. "I'll bet you somewhere in this damn country there's a whole warehouse full, if I could just find it."

"Mmm," said Schultz.

It was true, Miller searched diligently for a violin in every farmhouse and every village, interrogating the civilians with his "Fiddle? Violino?" and a violent pantomime of violin playing. Schultz did not know whether these civilians thought Miller really insane or just found it odd that a sergeant should want a violin, but they always looked startled and they never had a fiddle, nor even a guitar, which was Miller's second choice. Even if they had one they certainly wouldn't turn it over to him, thought Schultz, it's the silliest thing I ever heard of. This quest of Miller's, which had been going on for so long now, had no real purpose, since he could not play either instrument, and it irritated Schultz by its pointlessness. In the beginning he had questioned Miller carefully about his motives in the fiddle hunt, but the other was unable to explain it clearly. Miller had a scene in mind, a setting complete to the last detail, in which the fiddle was a necessary property. He saw himself sitting at night on a pile of crumbled stone and brick in a ruined, deserted village, playing the violin while rain came down in streams and torrents. The hoped-for-scene had become a part of the life around the three sergeants until they thought of it without surprise. Schultz could not approve, but he was resigned.

"Maybe when we get farther north," he said now, as he always did when Miller spoke of his wish. "They make the things up there somewhere."

It would be something to see, all right, he thought. Sleepyeye

Miller, who looked just a little like a clown in the early stages of making-up, huddled out in the rain squawking away on his fiddle. It would drive Moore really nuts. It would probably upset the whole damned war; in fact, Schultz thought happily, after all, they can't have things like that going on. It's the little things like that make the whole business bearable, especially when we're sitting around back here with nothing to look forward to but some officer coming down to check up on us. Why don't they keep those squirts busy swabbing out gun barrels or giving short arms or running around the country reading maps. They think an airplane is a truck, they want you to grease it all the time. It bothers the hell out of those people that the damn things will keep flying even if you don't strip them down completely every thirty days and check the tires every thirty minutes. The artillery! he thought with disgust, and sat up on his cot. So many better days to remember, and now this stupid politics! They win, we win, who cares? it's the same old dirty mess either way and a hell of a waste of time. After all, I'm thirty-eight years old as it is, he thought, and these jingo boys will push me around over here forever, piddling, doing nothing worth a damn, all of us just loafing in a barnyard full of manure and stink.

Schultz squeezed his lips together and puffed out his cheeks, then released his breath with a popping noise.

"I'm a Yankee Doodle Dandeeee," he sang aloud to the roof of the tent. "Yankee Doodle do or Dieeeeee."

He sat up, puffing and grunting, swung his feet to the ground and sat a moment, bent forward, staring vacantly, his forearms resting on his thighs and his puffy hands hanging between his knees.

"After the attack," he said calmly and surely, the voice of the narrator in a documentary motion picture. He bugged his eyes out and let his mouth fall open. "Ugh," he said. "Jeeze, Doc, will yah write a letter fer me? Why, certainly, son, boy, soldier, old man. Nurse! V-mail, pen, clipboard, right! Go ahead, son. Well, Doc, jus' tell my ole lady, the address is Saint James Infirmary, Route One, just tell the loveable ole bucket of guts . . ." his voice grew weaker, fading, his eyelids fluttered and almost closed, but the clipped and friendly voice of the doctor came back: "Yes? Yes? Nurse, hurry!" and then the stupid voice again, "Jus' tell 'er we held, Doc. Ahhhh!" and Schultz pretended to die, falling back on the cot.

"Balls," he said. "Balls, balls, balls. All the pawnbrokers' balls of Italee cannot sweeten this little harm. Sweetbreads for the general discontent. Just mountain oysters without a pearl in a carload. Pigs in pokes, looking for a home. *Vive le contrat social,* fella."

He got up, stepped briskly to Miller's cot, and shook hands with him.

"My name's Mock Clock," said Schultz. "Pardon me while I empty my bowels."

Again he walked briskly, purposeful and erect, to the tent opening where he halted, advancing one foot, leaning slightly backward, his thumbs hooked in the cloth belt of his fatigues, glaring scornfully out into the empty fields, his belly thrust forward.

"I am the creator and the destroyer," he said serenely. "All this means nothing to me, Caesar. Yes," he said, relaxing the pose, "I have my works. You know, I think maybe Moore has finally flipped his id, as we frolic here in the foothills and the tall ships grate upon the shingle, lifting with the tide, oh, the tide-o."

He cleared his throat and sang it softly:

"Oh, the tide-o, the tide-oooo," the notes dying softly and sadly in the quiet of the tent.

"All work and no jack makes dull a playboy," Schultz said, picking up his cloth fatigue cap from a disordered, leaning barracks bag. He tugged the cap crookedly onto his head and left the tent.

"It's just a matter of breeding, boy!" he called back to Miller. "Breeding and rank."

He walked toward a small structure like a battered upright coffin which stood fifty yards from the tent, walking at the brisk, fraudulent pace, head erect, shoulders back, the bill of the cloth cap bent and ragged over his squinted eyes. The fatigues clung to his middle as tightly as the casing on a sausage, but the cloth billowed around his knees and fell in loose folds over his buttocks, baggy, wrinkled and stained. He did not look back at the tent, the halftrack and the monoplanes.

Within ten yards the efficient, purposeful walk disappeared: Schultz began his usual amble, his shoulders slumped, walking on his heels, his feet pointed outward at every step. He kept his head erect, frowning and puckering his lips as though in disapproval, the stern overseer grown fat and almost drunken in a solitude the overseer had made for himself out of scorn and fear and boredom. When he reached the little structure he undid his fatigues, dropped them around his ankles, lowered his underwear and sat down.

This little building, formed of dented sheets of aluminum and scraps of green canvas, wired and twisted around metal tubing, was open on the side which faced the mountains and the village, and Schultz had an unobstructed view of this scene, as well as of the occasional peasant who walked across the fields carrying bundles of some sort of grain. As he sat there he exchanged pleasant gestures with the farm workers and called a greeting to those who passed within earshot.

The nicest spot in the whole country, thought Schultz, meaning the little building, which he called the Toonerville Trolley in spite of the messily lettered words, Short Arms Hotel, daubed on the canvas wall. There's no doubt about it, the Trolley makes all the difference. We're really living, kid, just like human beings, when you cart around a thing like this. We never had it so good, General, thanks very much, and thank you, Colonel, and thank you too, Quentin Reynolds, you've all been swell, really, we get along just fine.

If you could just armor this thing, Schultz thought, lighting a cigarette. A secret weapon! We'd be on Unter den Linden before we could shake the shitty end of a stick, which is what they'd give us to shake, and to hell with the psychological warfare branch. You wanta scare 'em, *scare* 'em, for God's sake, don't futz around with those silly pamphlets. On second thought, send us the pamphlets, we can do a little offset with them right here, and before that I could read them to Moore, he'd enjoy them very much. In fact, you're writing those for Moore, although you're going at it all wrong, of course, unless you figure all those birds over there are Moores, too, and it is an idea, Colonel, I've got to hand it to you there, all right. You should have Moore in a glass case at the Pentagon, pickled in rumors or in somebody's blood, preferably his own, you could use him as the national yardstick and throw away the platinum one, or whatever it's made out of. He probably expands and contracts quite a bit more than the old model, but you could run a graph on that, figure it all out like a new bridge, one you aren't quite certain about. Either that or give him a load test, see how much he can stand. That's the most practical approach, in fact it's so practical I'd say it was almost a field expedient. Somebody will get a promotion out of this, General, mark my words! Yessir, heads will roll somewhere . . .

And while we're at it, I've got another stunning idea, one for the national war monuments crowd. Yessir, this little old Trolley, right here, have this made up in marble and bronze and put it in the middle of Arlington. You may not realize it, honored sirs, but this is the real meat of the matter right here. Absolutely! I realize you've had to concern yourselves with the big picture and aren't too familiar with field matters, but I've been fortunate enough to relax with our boys, and this is it, right here. If you asked those boys, General, do you know what they'd tell you? Why, to a man, they'd say, shit, General, and no ifs, ands or buts about it. They're wonderful boys, General, and their hearts are pure. Oh, they're shy about it! They don't let just anybody see what's in their hearts,

General, you know that, they're just diamonds in the rough, those boys. You might think they're the most stupid, illiterate, bubble-headed bunch of jerks you ever saw, that half of them think they're in the Pacific and the other half thinks this is Louisiana maneuvers, but they're *boys,* General! Boys with false teeth and three wives and a dose of clap, General, that's all, and they're all going back and learn to read when this is over, probably by next Christmas, so they can find out what a dashing crew they were. It's not going to be easy, reading under a flat rock in West Virginia, but these boys can do anything. Look at what they've done already, stormed Fortress Europe, old *Festung Europa,* and didn't murder over half of themselves doing it. God knows what they did to the hun, General! It makes you feel proud, it gives you that old tingle jingle dingle, doesn't it. Citizen soldiers, screwing up the world fair . . .

"Good morning, son bitch."

Schultz started and looked up. An old man in a dirty black suit stood before him, not three feet away, smiling and nodding pleasantly.

"What the hell . . . ," said the mechanic.

"Please," the old man said, and he seized Schultz's right hand and shook it vigorously. "Welcome, welcome!"

"Let go of me!" shouted Schultz, and he jerked his hand away. "Don't you see what I'm doing? If you aren't the craziest damn people I ever saw . . ."

"Please," the visitor said again. "You make peepee? Very nice," and he smiled and bobbed his head at Schultz.

"God damn it," cried the mechanic, but he began to laugh and could not go on.

"Very nice," repeated the Italian, apparently reassured by Schultz's laughter.

"Whoooo," choked Schultz, leaning back weakly against the tin wall of the Trolley. "Varree nize."

"Hell, yes," the old man said, happy to find his American in such a jolly mood. "Me, New York, *millenovecento,*" and he carefully wrote "1900" in the air with his finger. *"Buono,* New York."

"Yes," gasped the mechanic, "varree nize," and he burst out with more laughter. If only this were Times Square, he thought, or the Astor bar, and he watched the old man unwrap a cloth bundle he was carrying and remove a full wine bottle.

"Drink," said the Italian, offering the red wine to Schultz with his right hand and patting himself on his stomach with his left. "Good, very nice."

"Wait a minute," said Schultz, and after a moment he stood and stepped out of the Trolley. "Come on," he said, taking the old man's arm and leading him toward the tent.

At the entrance he pushed the Italian ahead of him through the opening and pointed to Moore's cot, where the old man seated himself.

"What's going on?" asked Miller. He was seated on his cot with his bare feet drawn up on the edge and was dabbing a purple liquid between his toes with a ball of cotton.

"You just can't beat these people," Schultz said, and he fell on his cot and began laughing again.

"Drink," the old peasant said to Miller, holding out the bottle.

"Well!" cried the pilot, and he quickly thrust his feet into his shoes, rummaged in his tin box and brought out an aluminum canteen cup. "The cup that cheers!" and he filled the cup with wine, then returned the bottle.

The visitor sat rigidly on the edge of Moore's cot, his hands on his knees. His face, wrinkled like the meat of a walnut, was set in a rather foolish but pleasant look and he smiled very hard, showing the gaps in his rotten teeth. A strong smell of garlic, sweat and cheese came from him.

"Very nice," said Schultz, looking at the old man. "Very formal," and he reached for the bottle, produced his cup from under his cot and emptied the bottle into it.

"Where'd you pick up this character?" Miller asked, staring pleasantly at the civilian.

"In the Trolley," Schultz said. "He damned near got in the can with me. We'd have made a pretty little scene out there, in spite of all you hear about clean old men."

"Not very clean," said Miller, still looking at the Italian.

"No," said Schultz, "but he used to live in New York. He thinks New York is very nice," and he started laughing.

"Yes, very nice," said the old man, looking at Miller.

"You speak English?" Miller's sleepy eyes widened. "You know anybody around here has a fiddle?" He stood up and hopped around in front of the Italian, jiggling up and down.

"Please?" said the civilian, and his happy expression slackened.

"A fiddle!" said Miller. "A violino!" and he held his left arm out, fingers curled in toward the palm, and made wild sawing motions with his right hand over the elegantly crooked left elbow joint.

"Ah!" cried the old man, and he too made the movements with his skinny old arms. "No, I am not a violinist," he said in Italian, and looked sadly and warily at Miller.

"Hell!" said the pilot, hearing the "no" sound, and he sat down on his cot and drank from his canteen cup.

"Hope deferred," Schultz said. "Vino?" and he held out his empty cup to the old man.

"No vino," said the Italian, and he held up the empty wine bottle. "My house, plenty vino, plenty everything," he said, and then he put his fists to his temples with the forefingers extended stiffly upward and made butting motions with his head. Schultz and Miller looked at him, surprised. He then held his fists about two feet above the ground and made jerking motions toward the floor of the tent.

"A cow!" said Miller, delighted. "He wants us to come and eat a cow!" and he pulled off his shoes and began putting on his socks.

"Well, I'll be damned," Schultz said.

"Hell, yes," said the old man happily. "Good, hah? Good, Italia, no?"

"You betcha," said Schultz and he and Miller stood, ready, but the old man shook his head.

"*Doppo,*" he said, moving his hands up in a curve and then down. "*Doppo mezzogiorno,*" and he repeated the curving motion.

"This afternoon," Schultz said, smiling at the old man. "He wants us to come over to his house and eat a cow this afternoon. How about that!" and he nodded rapidly at the Italian, smiling and shaking hands with him. "*Buono,* very nice," he said. "*Sehr gut.*"

The old peasant stood up, still shaking hands with the mechanic, pulled him out of the tent and pointed toward the trees along the dry river. Beyond the streambed Schultz saw the roof of a building showing through the trees, and he nodded again at the old man.

"You bet," he said. "*Casa.* We come."

"*Doppo,*" the Italian said again, and he looked up at Schultz to make sure he understood.

"Absolutely," said Schultz, getting a little bored. "We'll be there," and he shook hands with the old man and went back into the tent. For a moment the visitor stood where Schultz had left him, his trouser legs and awkward, lumpy shoes visible from inside the tent, then he walked away.

"It's a barbecue or some damn thing," Schultz said to Miller, who had removed polish, brush and cloth from his tin box and was shining his shoes. "Anything for the *Americani,* you betcha. They must never have seen any before over at his place, the doughfeet must have gone through here in a hurry. Well, we'll fix that," and he stretched out on his cot to wait for the afternoon.

[IV] Sitting on the ground with the airplane's tire at his back, Moore was having his nightmare, staring at nothing.

. . . Help push plane out of wheelpits, walk around, shake wires, squat to look under control surfaces, grab wing tips, rock her on the fat tires. Satisfied, climb in, shrug into chute harness, fasten belt, Schultz swings prop, engine catches, rattling. Always rattles, nothing wrong there. After a minute reach overhead, twist switch from ON to R, then to L, back to ON, watching tachometer, from 1500 drops to 1200, okay. Wave to Schultz and Miller, I'll bet they go to the village, open throttle and taxi down to the end of the field, turn around, left brake is soft but not too soft, open throttle wide, release brakes, airplane starts to roll, getting speed, getting lift, grass is bumpy, then one last bump, starts to settle, doesn't, off and airborne . . .

He started a shallow, climbing turn to the northwest, looking back once at the field and the tent, growing smaller behind the rudder and the elevators. As the engine rattled, roared steadily in the climb he unfastened the safety belt and reached back, grunting, to the radio in the rear of his seat. He switched it on, fastened the belt again and took a set of headphones from a hook on the windowframe and clamped them over his thigh. A hand microphone hung from another hook, swinging and jiggling in the engine vibration.

He sat with his left hand on the red throttle knob, his right on the black rubber handle of the control stick, craning his head around to the left, now to the right, tipping his wing up to see under it, gazing up, down and on all sides of the monoplane. His eyes passed across the instrument panel as his head swung from left to right and he read the information there without pausing.

When he crossed the shoulder of the first mountain the altimeter read one thousand feet. He continued to climb as he flew up the valley, over service battery's village, the big mountain looming ahead of him through the propeller blur. It reared out of the haze in the valley, so much higher than its neighbors. He flew straight toward the mountain until it was about a thousand yards away, then turned and throttled back, flying slowly back and forth across the width of the valley.

The white buildings of the town were scattered at the mountain's base, where nothing moved. The buildings blazed in the sun, empty and white as chalk.

He pulled the earphones from his thigh and clamped them on his head, hearing again the buzzing static as they settled over his ears. He depressed a button on the microphone's handle and spoke against the harsh popping of the engine.

"Baker one able this is baker three able," he chanted, and released the button, waiting.

The buzzing in his ears accelerated, crackling, and changed into drawling, southern speech, metallic.

"Baker three able this is baker one able are you ready to observe," said the voice.

He pressed the button and answered, his voice faintly audible to him through the earphones, the crackling and the engine.

"One able give me coordinates," he said, and almost at once the voice crackled back to him.

"Three able daisy may from approximate coordinates," and a pause, "wuh-yun, ny-yun, forah, point, six-uh, tha-ree, seh-vun," saying it very carefully, and then, quckly and matter of fact, "can you observe, over."

He fumbled with a bulky map which he pulled from behind a control cable on the floor, unfolding it with one hand until he found the target on the map.

"One able one round smoke when ready," he said into the microphone, and the voice came back, "roger wait."

He looked up the valley, across the river, to a clump of trees along a small stream. He could not see the stream, but the map had a thin, blue thread printed on it, so the stream was there as far as he was concerned. He flew back and forth, glancing at the distant trees, waiting for the guns to receive the firing data, waiting for the smoke shell's white phosphorous plume in the valley.

North of the river, down the miles of valley, in the white dust roads, the blue asphalt highway, the hard line of the railway track, in the streets of the villages, he looked down on a deserted world, emptied of men and animals, where nothing moved, nothing showed itself. In the air he was a part of that emptiness and loneliness, he moved slowly along by himself. Although he felt the bareness of the sky he continued to look around him, not trusting the feeling, looking for something above him, under him, behind the elevators, sliding up at him from the left as he looked to the right. He seemed anxious, as though he had been waiting a long time, and was becoming impatient. His head checked in its swing and he stared at a patch of sky, frowning, his body taut against the safety belt and parachute straps. Then he looked away and continued his searching. Sometimes he reached out to touch the plastic windshield with a gloved finger, rubbing at a real or imagined grease spot. In the still air he fussed with the stabilizer control, rolling it a fraction of an inch forward or backward, balancing the airplane in its element as one may balance on a log half-submerged in water. He eased the throttle handle back, listening to the almost unnoticeable easing of the engine's labor, pushing it forward when the machine attempted to lose altitude, until he had combined engine and stabilizer in a delicate balance, the airplane flying slowly, its nose above the horizon, not climbing. And then something flashed in the trees along the invisible stream and he swung the airplane around with the rudder, reaching for the microphone before he heard the voice crackling in the earphones.

"Three able smoke on the way!" cried the voice, elated now, and he stared at the small, faraway trees, ignoring every other part of sky and earth, waiting until a huge boll of new cotton appeared magically in the valley, short of the trees, opened, grew into a thick white column and started to drift away, the smoke thinning until it was bluish, like milk.

"One able two hundred short," he said, and in less than a minute the second smoke shell burst beyond the trees, not more than fifty yards over.

"Repeat range six rounds h.e. adjusting gun only," he said, and soon there they were, the high explosive shells bursting among the trees, so he repeated the order twice. A cloud of brown dust hung in the trees, plummeting up abruptly as more shells exploded, and then an orange flame leaped up from the dust and glared for a moment before it flickered down to a small, guttering light. Heavy, greasy smoke began to roll up, boiling among the trees, lighted at intervals from within by orange and red fire.

"One able," he said, "cease firing, mission accomplished. A fire in the target area, looks like ammo."

"Roger, thank you and out," the voice said, sounding very close to him in the earphones, and he swung away and started home.

The first black burst was on his left and low. As he dived toward it he heard the crack of the explosion, too loud. He sat forward, straining against the belt, the throttle jammed open, swishing the plane from side to side with the rudder, urging the ground to come up to him.

Two more black smudges appeared in front of him suddenly, illogically, like wadded balls of black chiffon. He rushed toward them, saw them whip past the windshield, hearing the quick blam blam of the bursts, then pulled back on the stick, leveling out a hundred feet above over the highway.

It wasn't praying, he was too busy for that, but a frenzied series of calculations zipped through his mind, weighing this maneuver against that, thinking ahead to the hills which he must climb over, trying to keep his speed above normal with a slight, very slight dive and yet not lose all altitude, and mixed in with it a wild hope, a wish to be missed by the black burst, to have the gunners lose sight of him in the broad valley, to have them drop a shell at the breech, jam the mechanism, miscalculate . . . and finally he came to the low hills and lifted the airplane over them with a strong pull on the control stick, dropping down beyond them with enough speed to stay in the air, no more. Another shallow dive and the monoplane lost its sluggishness and he was rattling along over the highway again, over service battery's village, over the mountain shoulder and home, curving down in a diving turn to the field, where the Cub ran along with a rumbling sound, then turned with a blast of engine noise and taxied toward the tent. Head out the open door, squinting in the prop blast, let her settle easy into the pits . . . engine off and sit for a moment in the silence before climbing out, stiff.

Telling Schultz, "That was one hour and thirty-five minutes," looking at the watch, "you log it and I'll write in the mission."

[v] Moore was breathing heavily, as though he had run a long way and had fallen under the airplane wing to rest. His eyes were shiny and wet and in his partly open mouth his tongue was swollen and dry. He had drawn his legs up against his stomach and was gripping his knees with his hands.

He relaxed as he became aware of himself, feeling like a man who watches a motion picture nervously, forgetting the excitement is on film, restricted to the screen and not able to reach him. He pulled a tattered cigarette package from his pocket and lighted a cigarette, twisting his lips because the brand was one of the unfamiliar ones which he despised. The sight of one of these strange tobacco packages always gave him a faint feeling of alarm, it made him think of easy graft somewhere, of rich, fat men laughing at him as they hoarded millions of good cigarettes.

This is going to be a terrible day, he thought, and threw the cigarette away, watching it smolder in the field, under the hot sun. And then he heard something, and looked up as Schultz and the old man came out of the tent.

Oh, what's he up to now, he wondered, and the anxieties of the ground, the distrust and doubt came rushing back into him as though he had not relived the hour and thirty-five minutes in the valley. He wanted to stay under the wing forever, out of it, finished with it, but then he sighed, and groaned, and stood up. After hesitating, he went over to the tent and ducked inside.

Miller looked up, then continued to work on his shoes with the brush. Schultz was lying on his cot: he pursed his lips and grunted, without opening his eyes.

Moore looked at them quickly, trying to guess what had happened.

"What did that old man want?" he said. "You drinking now, in the middle of the morning? What if the captain comes down here, you know when we're out on a rest like this he's liable to start poking around—"

"We're resting!" Schultz said. "We're not drunk, we're just resting. In a minute we'll probably be writing V-mails, begging for fruit cakes, for Christ's sake. If the captain comes down here he can censor the damn things, unless you'd like to do it yourself."

"Well, it'll be your problem, not mine," Moore said.

"That's right," Schultz said, not opening his eyes. "That's exactly right. I'm glad you understand it," and he broke wind noisily.

Moore wrinkled his nose in disgust and turned to Miller.

"Did you watch him? I mean, he didn't take anything, did he? That's all they're after, you know, they'll steal anything . . ."

"He invited us to a barbecue," Miller said, admiring the sheen on his shoes.

"What? What are you talking about?" Moore noticed Miller's shoes for the first time. "What are you doing that for? You know we're not supposed to leave the area, they might want us to fly somebody over to corps."

Schultz gritted his teeth. Leave the area! What the hell is that, anyway. You can't leave this area without a boat or a B-17, unless you're dead, and even then it's a relative thing.

"It's just across the river," he told Moore. "The old man has a cow he wants us to help him eat, he's trying to be varree nize. He used to live in New York."

"New York!" cried Moore. "They all say that. They all tell you they lived in Brooklyn, they think that makes everything all right. The fact of the matter is they lost their war, that's all. If it weren't for that they'd be shooting at us right now," and he threw himself on his cot, face down. "I don't think we should leave the planes," he said.

Schultz made a face which meant, nobody invited *you*, you know, but he said nothing. Miller had finished polishing his shoes and, after admiring them once more, placed them carefully under his cot and began rummaging in a canvas bag.

"They don't have barbecues over here anyway," Moore said.

"They got a cow and vino, the old man said," and Miller's expression showed he felt that was enough, or almost enough. The rest he would take care of by himself.

"It's just a party of some kind," Schultz said. "The old man's just trying to be nice to us, that's all."

"What for?" asked Moore, turning to the mechanic. "Did you think of that? These people don't like us, they never have. They probably want to get us away from here so they can come over and steal everything we have."

"Let 'em have it," said Schultz. "The Army will give us some more. They've got plenty of everything, even pilots. They're plowing 'em under, I hear, back in Oklahoma."

It's not as if I wanted them to do anything for me, thought Moore. He watched Schultz, the closed eyes, the twitching, puffy cheeks, the half-smothered snorts. Schultz thrashed grumpily on his cot and then rolled over, his face to the wall of the tent.

Moore looked away and sighed. Miller pulled a clean cotton shirt from his blue barracks bag and spread it out on his cot, smoothing it with his hands, trying to flatten the wrinkles, and the sight made Moore quietly furious, since it smacked of a three-day pass. Actually, Moore told himself, we might go back up to the line at any minute. Any minute they might come down here and tell us we're going back up there. Why can't Miller and Schultz think of that? Why can't they ever understand what a serious business this is? Why don't they ever see the war the way I do? One afternoon back in the winter he had been patrolling above the monastery when the Arkansas voice crackled in his earphones with warning: German fighters were reported coming down the valley from the north. Moore dived away from the monastery across the valley and into a bowl-shaped pocket in the mountains, a huge cleft in the rocks a quarter of a mile wide which plunged clear to the valley, almost three thousand feet below. He circled in this cleft in a tight turn, hiding in it until they would tell him over the radio that the valley was clear, that he could come back and finish adjusting the guns on a town, and after he had made four of these turns (which were tricky to make in the cleft because air rushed down from the mountain into it like water into a sluice, and was turbulent), he noticed something foreign in the snow and rocks, something waving to him.

He looked as he came around again and saw a soldier on a ledge perhaps fifty feet wide, up to his crotch in snow, holding one end of a pup tent. The other end of the little tent stood out from him in the wind, snapping and flapping like a flag or a line of washing, the canvas viciously alive in the man's hands, as though it would tear itself from him at any moment.

He went around again, staring at the soldier, who stood without moving except for his arms, which were being jerked and shaken by the tent. He looked as though he might stand that way until the wind quit, since it was obviously impossible for him to handle the tent alone. Had the tent almost blown away from its moorings, or was he just now trying to set it up? Where were his friends, and how did he expect to peg it down in the snow and rock?

As Moore circled he realized the man was looking at him. At times they were within seventy-five or a hundred feet of each other or even closer as the bucking air currents tore at the tent and at the airplane controls, and Moore stared back into the soldier's face, neither man making a sign of recognition or of friendship. The man on the ledge appeared numbed, resigned to this fantastic job of holding on to the tent all alone on a mountainside, he seemed beyond help, almost scornful of it, even if help could come to him. He looked at Moore in the airplane as if this was perfectly ordinary, as if he was not in the least surprised or angered by the tent nor by Moore's circling, so close he could have hit the airplane with a stone but so far from him that it would have taken him twenty-four hours of climbing, scrambling, falling and walking to arrive at Moore's tent, which was ten minutes away in the monoplane.

And so Moore went around and around, looking at the soldier, the soldier looking at him, dumbly, each unable to communicate with the other, the man on the ledge even unwilling to do so, apparently, standing there in the snow as though Moore and the airplane were parts of a nightmare which would go away eventually, keeping his eye on the nightmare but certainly not about to greet it, and before he could stop himself Moore began laughing.

He circled again and again, laughing at the man on the ledge in his ridiculous, pathetic predicament, turning his head away from the ledge when he came near it so the soldier could not see that he was laughing or feel that he was laughing, and then the clear signal had come on the radio and he had turned back into the valley, not knowing if the man had known he was laughing nor whether or not he had held on to the tent, his home.

I hope he didn't see me laugh, thought Moore.

This doesn't seem so bad, when you think of things like that, he told himself, and he balanced the man on the ledge, all the men in the mountains against Schultz and Miller, but then he thought of the old man and the cow, and it was no balance at all, they would go across the river and he would go with them, so all the rest was wasted.

"When are you going," he said, his voice running downhill, not like a question. He spoke to Miller, but Schultz rolled over and looked at him.

"This afternoon, sometime," he said. "Want to come?"

Moore shrugged, why not, and turned on his side with his back to Schultz. They might even go all the way to Naples, he thought, if I weren't along, and he tried to relax and sleep. He no longer slept at night for more than fifteen or twenty minutes at a time and he wanted to sleep now, for the afternoon across the river.

[vi] I hope they don't boil the damn thing, thought Schultz. Of course it's bound to be as old as Mussolini, maybe it'll be too tough to do anything else. Maybe they'll fry it, though, that wouldn't be as bad as boiling it, or maybe they'll roast it, on an iron spit. That's all right, if you know what you're doing. Just so they don't boil it. He began to think of food, of how it could be, although he knew it wouldn't be like that at all.

Lying on his cot he imagined the farmhouse kitchen bins full of firm, clean potatoes, and crowded strings of onions, garlic, peppers and mushrooms hanging from the ceiling over the deep, gaping fireplace, and in the cellar there were great, fragrant casks of good, nutty wine, both red and white. Hard crusted, freshly baked loaves of long, hot bread lay on a scrubbed table in a still life of fat, scarlet radishes, fresh from the moist earth which still clung to their roots in tiny clots of mud. There were big, sweet onions in piles, bunches of crisp celery, chicory and heads of tender leaf lettuce, all strewn over the raw white wood of the table in an abundance which was beautiful. And meat he wanted in the farmhouse, all sorts of meat, from whole sides of fat beef, slabs of pork, bacon and heavy curves of chops to freshly killed chickens and rabbits, stuffed with garlic and vegetables, ready for the ovens. The farm woman would smile, delighted to have him at the table, giving him little glances of appreciation and admiration (not bad looking, either!), as her husband sat with him, filling his glass and slapping him on the back in a burst of affection and good feeling. Platters and bowls of steaming, delicious, mouth-watering food would come to the table, some of it entirely unknown to him. Meats in tangy, thick brown sauces, fried chops, broiled steaks, juicy roasts, bowls of fried chicken and fried potatoes, roast chickens and rabbits, wooden bowls of salads, each green leaf coated with oil and vinegar, and a heavy, lopsided glass filled with the splendid wine. After eating he would light a good cigarette from a fresh, rich-smelling pack, and drink cups of strong black coffee with small glasses of fiery, satisfying grappa. Then he would be shown into a white-walled bedroom, the plaster unblemished and spotless, the bed covered with a lace spread. He would slip down between the cool, starched sheets and sleep, sleep, sleep, for days on end, for there would be no bedbugs in the bed. When he wakened he would take a scalding bath, then dress in clean clothing and go in to breakfast. It would be time to start on the wife then, too.

Maybe, thought Schultz, maybe I might take the bath first, then have the food, but he knew it wouldn't be that way. He hated to think of lying on those clean sheets with his dirty body, but the bath would have to wait.

What a lot of crap! he told himself, and moved impatiently on the cot, feeling the sweat trickling across his stomach. We'll go over there and drink that acid and catch fleas from somebody and then we'll come back and puke all night and in the morning Moore will look like somebody's mother, seen through a bloody caul. Just The Boys, The Boys From Gladland, out on an innocent frolic, the nation's ambassadors as busy as a bucket of snakes.

And now Moore's in it, too, thought Schultz, the white hope is going to drop his sword for a minute and go look out the castle window. No good can come of that, no good at all, he won't like it and he'll tell us how much he doesn't like it and he's liable to ruin it for everybody trying to find a Hidden Meaning in all that rut and bellywash. They should weld him into the airplane and never let him out, feed him though a hose. In there he can't bother anybody, short of killing them. He probably does that very well, I don't know. How many of them are like that, do you suppose? More on the other side, probably, but enough here, too. The

Believers. They learned to listen and to read about the time Lindbergh flew to Paris and it's been going on ever since then on both sides and it really is remarkable, it's so screwy it's fascinating. Somehow or other they see and hear exactly what they're supposed to and nothing else, as though the world was giving it to them through electrodes built into their skulls. They want everything already canned and labeled, like a supermarket, you can take your pick, although the choice is limited by management, of course. A stabilized economy without any economists. How did they do it, anyway, or did it just happen, like Babe Ruth and the synthetic barroom Irishmen and the Ku Klux Klan . . .

No, Moore did it to himself, decided Schultz, I guess they all do, it's something in the air, they don't know any better and they wind up liking it. What I should do, he told himself, feeling a faint stir of interest at the idea, what I really should do is undertake the de-education of Moore, I should straighten him out about things. He's just a kid, after all, there's still some hope, if I could just get him to listen to me and really bear down on him . . . wouldn't his parents be surprised! Send us the boy, we send you the jerk, the no-man, he doesn't give a damn how much you holler, you can take the Legion and the PTA and the Optimists Club and shove 'em up your ass, he just wants to be left alone. It's an idea, anyway, it might keep us amused.

If we left Moore behind this afternoon maybe they'd steal away with him, he thought, up into the hills like the banditti used to do. He could get everything on a good, sound basis up there, hang somebody and raise the price of cheese, be a real, saddlesore military government man. The trouble with you is, Moore, you enlisted, or rather, there's something wrong with you, so you enlisted. You enlisted and you're from the South, where the boll weevils and the corn pone and the fried crap and the volunteers come from. You think you're an aristocrat, but there aren't any aristocrats. That whole country down there is one big privy, with everybody scribbling dirty words on the walls and pretending they didn't, you silly son of a bitch, just a tribe of tumblebugs, and then they all run out and enlist. Practically every volunteer in the Army comes from down there, what're they after? You'd think they had some kind of wobblejawed, barefoot, illiterate tradition about it, a bareassed, inbred Junker crowd, only in this one everybody's a buckbottom private. Generations of pfc's, for Christ's sake, and occasionally a genius rises among them and makes sergeant, after he learns to smoke instead of dip and figures out what his Army handkerchief is for. Why do they do it? Is this so much better than chopping cotton or squatting around the square? They must still be trying to prove something, if it's not just getting away from something, they must still be trying to show somebody, maybe themselves, that what happened in the 1860's was just carelessness, or maybe they think it's still the same war, and what the hell, I guess it is. But no, decided Schultz, most of them never heard of that war or this one either, they think it's a big shivaree, I gonnies, an organized ride out in the country, they figure they're all going to hide up in the woods and shoot twenty-twos at the church bell while the revival is going on, just to devil the congregation. The only thing wrong is there isn't enough whiskey and the congregation shoots back, to beat hell. Then it's too late and they don't like it, just like they didn't like it in the sixties when the coon hunt got caught out in a tornado and the coon got away and there was nothing to do but go home and cuss at the coon. You can't cuss at a tornado very long or very well, it's a freak of nature, it could happen to anybody, but that goldurned coon, that impudent scannel! They've been looking for that coon to come sneaking back ever since, and every once in a while somebody on the other side of the ridge let's out a yell, "Ah seen him, ah seen the son of a bitch!" and whoopee! whambam, drop the turnip greens and fatback and bust out the door, light runnin', man! and down the holler and out of sight in a cloud of dried cowshit. That's why the army gives 'em antitetanus shots right away, before they even scrape the dung out from between their toes. And the ones like Moore, the ones that have moved into town and are now a little scared of their relatives out in the country, worried about "that Joyner blood," they're just as feeble-minded, they go to "A & M" or good old state u if papa has the money and then they're worse off than their cotton-headed cousins out in the cane bottoms. The thing is, they don't know it, that's the advantage the educated man has down there or anywhere else, unless the schooling doesn't quite take, but it usually does, just like the antitetanus. You may puke for a while, but you get over it. Lie down, get a little rest, you'll be all right. If it keeps coming back on you, that's too bad, it's time you realized you're alive, not in paradise, you bastard, you fink, you stinkfingered bum, you satchel-headed human being, you. Take that! Biff bam blooey, and a beer-bottle up your twat if you don't like it. That's what made budwiser, that's what made Saint Louis famous when Mark Twain went steaming by from Hannibal with a bone on or in his teeth or whatever it was, or is. It's that "Joyner blood," boy, even Marse Robert had it for all his fine manners, and probably Traveler had it, too, it's like a strain of syph, it runs through the whole country down there. Bad blood, and a wild mongoose! Idiots, a whole tribe of pinheaded cretins, there's nothing worth a damn south of Cairo, Illinois; it should be fenced off and then burnt off, and to hell with the volunteers and the butternut boys in gray. They can have their war somewhere else, they can even have this one, but I'm going across the river this afternoon whether yellowsash likes it or not and I hope I get so drunk I don't know where he is or I am.

Schultz cleared his throat noisily.

"Heil Hitler in case we lose," he said, and made a determined effort to go to sleep.

[VII] Miller lay neatly on his cot, his hands clasped on his flat stomach, his head pillowed on a small canvas bag stuffed with winter clothing. This position allowed his sleepy-looking eyes to gaze at his feet, the toes smeared with the purple liquid which was said to cure athlete's foot, a condition which Miller did not have. A medic had given him the liquid when Miller had seen it in his kit and asked what it was, and he used it as a prophylactic measure, always the soldier making use of everything around him, saving up against the catastrophe which was always to be expected.

Looks like I'd been walking in grape juice, he thought, and the idea pleased him. It would be fun to go swimming in a tank full of grape juice, maybe with a woman; it would be sticky. Wouldn't it look funny when we got out! He turned his head to tell Schultz about it, but decided the mechanic was asleep.

Maybe there'll be some women at the barbecue. Plenty to eat and drink and some women, and someplace to take them, where we can get away from Moore. He worries too much, he's from Texas, he thought, remembering what Schultz had said, and that made him think of the trip to Wichita Falls.

She was a cute little twirp, wandering around the hotel in shorts, or was that in Duncan? No, that's where it was, we landed out on that fellow's airport, the private one, but it wasn't much of a strip. His wife drove us into town in a Cadillac with the back seat all greasy and full of oil well tools. They had two iceboxes as big as the ones at Schofield Barracks and one of them was full of beer, no meat, no milk, nothing but beer. That's where it was, all right, I found her in the hotel where we went after the rich guy's wife got mad at Schultz. A newlywed, just walking around in that hotel hall. I guess that was the best thing I ever fell over. She was crying at first and she took me down to her room and told me to look in, through the transom because the key was inside, and there was her husband, passed out on the bed with his tallywhacker sticking up in the air. Ho! Miller smiled and rubbed his feet together, remembering the carnival atmosphere of the wartime hotel. You could've stacked arms with that thing and he never would have known the difference. When we finally got the door open and got in bed he didn't even roll over. I wish I'd had a fiddle then, playing the fiddle to her while he lay there like that! Ah, ho! Don't worry about a thing, I told her, just keep moving, keep moving! He'll think he's on a train! She had to laugh at that, I remember, but it would've been better with a fiddle, and it did not occur to him that he had never been taught to play the violin, he never thought of that at all.

I can't figure it out, thought Miller, staring at his feet, I thought these people ran around playing music all the time and here there ain't a fiddle in the whole country, they don't even sing. What a dead-assed bunch, and he thought with sweet longing of the saloons, beer parlors and dance halls of his native land, of the young girls in sweaters and the endless supplies of liquor stacked up behind the bars, the glare of neon and the jukebox jazz. And outside in the huge, black Oklahoma night or the chill bright Colorado night or wherever it might be, the night different in each place but the rest of it alike, were the cars, the taxis, the white stucco motels waiting with dim, naked bulbs burning over doors, the hospital smell of Lifebuoy soap and then next morning the barracks, the camp, where the outside couldn't touch you. You darted out at it, gaily, taking what you wanted, then skipped back through the gate and were safe, a joke on somebody! In a week, a month, you were gone, gone away, leaving nothing, missing nothing, you had it all with you in sacks and a foot locker, the wind blowing across a parade ground, tossing paper along on a vast, silent airfield, because you weren't there anymore and so nothing was there. A dozen, twenty Millers left in twenty places but he moving on with the crowd, across the big, friendly country, never quite a part of it, flicking out at it on weekends, then running back inside, happy, not thinking of next year or even next week.

I hope Moore's wrong about it, that they do know how to barbecue, thought Sergeant Miller, trying carefully to place the toes of his right foot between the toes of his left foot, like weaving a basket, and then he stopped and looked up at the roof of the tent, his eyes widening as though he had been actually sleeping. Did the old man say it was a barbecue? I can't remember if he did or not, but didn't Schultz say that's what it was? Anyway, something will happen, he decided, and went back to weaving with his toes.

[viii] Moore was in the grandstand of the ball park in his home town, watching a rodeo. It was hot, the dust spurted up under the plunging feet of horses and drifted slowly into the stands, choking, dirtying, settling on the red, white and blue bunting which was tacked up everywhere, coating red faces, sweating necks, collecting on hats and white shirts. The crowd ignored the dust, they strained forward toward the men and animals threshing around in the dirt, and Moore felt he was the only one who noticed the thick clouds which settled over them all, plugging their nostrils and ears. He was wearing a white linen suit, he could remember when his father had bought it for him at Goldstein's for a trip to Galveston, and he kept brushing dust from his coat and trousers, his sweating palms smearing the dust into mud. The girl sitting next to him was the most popular in town, he had never been out with her before although he knew who she was and she knew who he was, and he noticed that in the suffocating heat she was wearing a tweed suit which looked expensive and very eastern, not like Texas at all. Probably home from school for the holidays, but why is it so hot? And what are we doing at a rodeo, I never went to rodeos. He tried to ask the girl, but she was unable to hear him, she was screaming and cheering at the men in the arena, lean, western men, whose thin, sharp faces could be seen even through the dust, even in the shadows cast by their big hats as they performed feats of brute strength among the dust clouds. They seized the horns of ferocious steers as big as locomotives and

overturned them onto the earth, where the steers' legs waved helplessly in the air and their shriveled bull pizzles were terribly exposed to the avid crowd in the stands. He risked a quick glance at the girl, expecting her to be embarrassed, but she was staring down into the arena like everyone else, admiring, eager . . . and now there were wild horses, with men of wire and muscle astraddle them, arching, bowing, leaping madly while the men clung like bloodsuckers to their backs, their skins seeming stitched, melted into the skin of the horses. Obscene! Moore opened his mouth to cry out, but his tongue was too dry, his throat was coated with gritty, abrasive dust, and at once the men were naked astride the horses and the animals began to copulate, furiously, insanely, the arena was filled with them, they crashed into the boards at the foot of the grandstand and rebounded, not ceasing their mad piston action for an instant. The crowd was on its feet, roaring, the touchdown roar, the knockdown bellow, blood, blood, even the girl was standing in her expensive tweed suit, straining forward on her brown and white pumps, they ignored Moore, who sat on the splintery board seat, his loins shriveled, chilled with cold, dead sweat, alone, terribly, fatally alone in the dust and bedlam. I'm not what they want! he screamed, but could not hear it, and then the rotten, dessicated wooden plank crunched under him and he was falling into the darkness under the stands, plummeting down through the shadows and the smell of feet, of year-old urine, of a thousand crowds and a million rotted hot dogs until with a sickening, upward swoop he lost consciousness. . . .

He was lying on the worn, sour earth under the grandstand. The hot wind tumbled old candy wrappers against him, where they clung like flotsam, piling up against his side. The roar of the crowd sounded distant, like faraway surf, rising and falling in slow, regular and restrained rhythm. He started to sit up, putting his right hand out to steady himself, and felt it sink into something warm and soft and repulsive, and looked to see that he had placed his hand wrist deep in a pile of human dung. Jerking his hand back as though from a heap of snakes, he cleaned it as best he could with the candy wrappers and got to his feet, holding the hand away from his side, with the stiff fingers spread wide apart. Overhead in the dusty gloom thousands of legs hung down through the board seats, male and female, fat and lean and hairy, twitching and damp with excitement, looking separate and weirdly complete without their bodies. Under this prickly roof of bony, crooked sausages he wandered, crying up to them for help, stumbling on old beer bottles, stopping at each concrete pillar to wipe his filthy hand against the cool, rough surface until he came to one pillar which was hot, columnar, throbbing, and he drew back in horror and fear, turning to run. Then, far away down the long, dim gallery roofed with the tiny legs, he saw something white and blurred, stirring heavily in the dirty twilight. Dread poured into his bloodstream, chilling him, turning his bowels to liquid, and he began to move, slowly, on heavy, weighted feet, then quickly, quickly, faster, until he was hurtling through the gloom, away from the white blur, afraid to look behind him but feeling it there, gaining, drawing closer, and then he looked back and it was on him.

"EEEEEUH!" screamed Sergeant Moore. Schultz jerked his hand from the pilot's shoulder.

"What the hell!" Schultz cried, stepping back quickly from Moore's cot. Moore moaned, slowly opening his eyes, his eye-sockets gleaming with sweat, his fists clenched under his chin and his legs drawn up to his stomach.

"My *God*, man!" Schultz stared angrily at Moore. "What did you do that for? You like to scared me to death!"

"Unh," said Moore, licking his lips. He sat up and stared at Schultz, not fully awake, his eyes drugged but frightened.

"I'm sorry," he said after a moment. "What is it?" and he looked around the tent as though expecting to see something new there.

"Time to go," said Schultz. "It's almost two o'clock."

He tugged at the enormous nylon scarf he had wrapped around his neck, the one he had cut that morning from the parachute, pushing the ends down inside the front of his greasy coveralls. The shining white stuff stood up almost to his ears, covering his neck like a gigantic, loosened bandage, and Moore, trying to forget his nightmare, thought of W. C. Fields as Micawber, looking up at Schultz's puffy, foolishly arrogant face above the wadded stock of the scarf.

"You'll burn up in that thing," Moore said, sitting up on his cot. "What are you wearing it for?" and he hoped Schultz would remove it, leave the uneasy thing in the tent.

"Because it's clean," Schultz said irritably. "It feels good. The Arabs do it," he told Moore. "It actually keeps you cool, something like this," and it gives us something to talk about and it will be my contribution to the barbecue, he thought. You dress up a little for something like this, you never know what's going to happen, right when you least expect it, and he felt pleasantly excited.

"All right, men," he said, looking sternly at Miller. "Pro kits? Raincoats? Helmet liners? Shoes? All right, men, follow me," and he turned and left the tent, followed by Miller in his glittering shoes and clean, wrinkled khakis.

For a moment Moore remained on his cot, not caring, beyond it, and then the panic came back and he scrambled out of the tent and into the glare, following Schultz and Miller.

I should have brushed my teeth, he thought, tasting the sour bitterness in his mouth, but he kept going across the field, hurrying a little to catch up with the others.

[IX] They walked abreast in the stubble field, the sun struck at them, the landscape wavered and floated, and in the far, far distance, northward up this valley which somewhere met the other, crucial valley, the inaccessible mountains looked flat, thin and grainy in the haze. The air smelled of heat, mountains and very fine, faint old dust, the dust of rock and clay, of grain and dried, ancient dung, a rich, sweet and rotten smell like an Algerian vineyard.

After Schultz had taken a dozen steps the white scarf around his neck was clammy and adhesive. The nylon did not absorb the sweat as cotton would have and he felt the drops rolling down his back and chest, tickling like chaff under his coveralls.

I might as well be at a lynching in Friar's Point, Mississippi, he thought, it's as hot as a tin roof in New Braunfels. Right now I'd like to be in the ugliest spot on earth, the St. Louis Union Station. I'd take a cab to the Coronado and go down in the cellar, down in the Coal Hole, and spend the afternoon telling lies, coveralls, nylon and all, and I'd try to forget all about the Union Station, all the things that have happened to me in the Union Station. Or maybe The Kansas City Union Sation, where you come out the doors and look across the street at Foch's phallic symbol up on the hill, the silo, the never no more. That's typical; they turned off their eternal fire and chiseled Lindbergh's name off of it when the war started, and you couldn't have the Mikado and the Lunts had to quit that business about the Russians in Finland. The fire was steam with colored lights on it, the Japs could see that from Pearl Harbor, you betcha. Anyway, I could take a cab from there in the late afternoon, the sun just down behind the post office, and go to the Peanut, out in the garden in back, on the gravel and the tin tables, and I'd take this scarf and hang it on Ardonia's meek brown neck and I'd say there, there it is, Ardonia, this is how it was, like a nylon fleece, and I'd say dear, it was hell, you can't imagine the funny people I ran into, bring me an order of fried baby bottoms and a glass of beer and I'll tell you all about it. The happy sound of walking on the clean gravel, and the cold tin of the tables in the shade, and the cold, cold beer going down, biting and fizzy, and Ardonia like new chocolate in her starched blue uniform, with the scarf hanging down like something out of a church.

And that's not southern, thought Schultz, glancing quickly at Moore, and that's why I like it, I didn't know it then but that's one of the reasons.

"Is it true what they say about Dixie," he chanted, almost singing it, "does the sun really shine all the t-i-i-i-me. Does it, Moore? Is it seven, seven times hotter than it oughta be, little Moses?"

"All right," Moore said, not looking at Schultz.

"Folks keep eatin' possum till they can't eat no more," Miller said, very happy to remember the line, and he looked from Schultz to Moore, half expecting them to join him in song.

"Never mind that nigger stuff," Moore said, but he still did not look at the others. "That's the only thing you people ever heard of, the nigger part."

"What's a possum?" said Miller. "I hear about that all my life, but what is it, anyway?"

"It's a rat," said Schultz. "A great, big rat, as big as a fox terrier."

"What? You mean to tell me it's a rat? You mean to say they eat rats? A big mouse?"

"They'll eat anything down South, where've you been. They even eat snakes, they can them and sell them all over the damn place."

"Well, for Christ's sake . . ."

"Just like a Vienna sausage. Didn't you ever have a snake sandwich? You should have told me, they had them in Whiskey Falls . . . ask him, he probably used to take 'em to school before the hot lunch program came in . . ."

". . . program?"

"Never mind, you got it this morning. You're a moron, he's about right."

"Fuck you."

"Never mind, I said."

They stepped from the low, crumbling bank into the riverbed, a glaring, powdery white sheet of pitted rock. They crossed it and climbed the opposite bank. Within twenty steps they were out of the aged tree line and approaching the farmhouse.

It was a large, two-story building, worn and softened, with a broken tile roof, or roofs, since each room appeared to have been conceived and built separately. Some of the bricks were thin, others thick, and they varied in color from pale bleached yellow to hearty raw reds and faded pinks. Even the newest bricks looked old, and the building gave the impression of gradually fading, settling in upon itself, until in time it would become indistinguishable from the earth under it and around it. The sergeants had seen a thousand like it.

Two long, narrow outbuildings like stables or slave quarters extended from the rear wall of the main building to form a courtyard, with a stone fence and gate at the open end. The noise of an Italian crowd came from this enclosure, increasing in volume as several small boys rushed through the gate to tell those within that the Americans were coming. There were shouts, and a dozen heads appeared above the wall, looking at the sergeants, who had halted near the main building, waiting for something, a sign, the first movement of the afternoon.

Suddenly, the face of an old woman appeared in a window almost at Schultz's elbow. She glared at him, then withdrew her head and they heard her shouting in Italian inside the house.

"Here are the barbarians!" the old woman cried.

"Silence!" a male voice answered at once. "You fool, these are Americans."

"Aiuh!" the woman said, a despairing grunt. "What's the difference? These have rubber soles on their shoes, that's the difference. They'll want the same things."

"I ask you to curb your filthy tongue," the man said. "These are my guests, this is my house."

"Guests!" screamed the woman. "You'll have a brothel if you bring in such guests as these, idiot!"

"Would that I had left you in the one where I found you!" shouted the man, and there was a great clash of falling pans.

"Better I than your daughters, then, and your granddaughters," the woman wailed, and more pots clanged on a stone floor. "Why not sell us all, put us in the Via Roma naked to the stomach, with jet beads on our underwear?"

"Mother of God," said the man. "Sainted Mary."

"What the hell are they yelling about?" said Miller. "Must be something to do with chow."

The old man came out of the open door and yelled something over his shoulder before smiling and nodding at the Americans.

"You are most welcome," he said in Italian. "Please pay no attention to that filth in the kitchen, she's just a nervous old slut. My wife," he added apologetically, and still in Italian, "but she did not go to the great New York with me."

"Good old New York," Miller said, hearing the words.

The old man seized Miller's elbow and pulled him rapidly along to the gate in the stone fence. The crowd in the enclosure sent up a great shout and surrounded them.

"The Americans! The Americans!" they cried. Old men and women, young men and girls and children barely able to walk surged happily around the startled sergeants. Miller tried to free his arm, but the old man increased the grip of his knotted fingers.

Moore decided at once that everyone present was drunk except the children. The older men and women were drunkest, and several brown-skinned, wrinkled old women in rusted black lay on the ground next to the buildings. A smell of raw wine, cheese and garlic came from the excited people in the farmyard in a wave as solid as the heat Moore had felt under the airplane wing.

"What a barbecue!" Schultz shouted, grabbing a full wine bottle from a smiling man who immediately offered him another.

"Wait a minute!" cried Moore, scowling and shaking his head at a young woman who held out a bottle and then pressed a full glass to his lips. He choked, spluttering, and the bright red wine splashed down his coveralls. The drops which struck the ground were sucked in at once by the dried earth. Miller and Schultz laughed at him, so did the girl, so did everyone but the old man, who looked worried and mopped ineffectually at Moore's clothing with a dirty rag which he pulled from his pocket.

"What's going on here?" Moore shouted at him. He grabbed the rag from the old hand and threw it on the ground, then seized the black-sleeved arm and shook it. "What are you people up to, anyway?"

"Please forgive her, Captain," the old man said in Italian. "She's just trying to make you welcome, you know."

He turned suddenly to the girl and raised his hand as though to strike her.

"Clumsy imbecile!" he shouted. The crowd laughed, and the girl stuck her tongue out at the old man.

"A father's curse," she said, and spat on the ground at his feet. The crowd laughed again. The old man grinned and shrugged his shoulders.

Moore seized his arm again.

"Listen," he said. "Tell me what's going on. You can speak English. You said you'd been to New York, didn't you? This isn't just a party, is it?"

"Yes, yes, New York," said the old man, bobbing his head rapidly up and down. "Magnificent! You know Via Mulberry Street?"

"Come on!" shouted Miller above the crowd noise. "Grab some bottles and let's sit down somewhere."

He and Schultz had already started elbowing their way toward the other end of the farmyard. Moore started to object, but the girl who had spilled the wine on him took his arm and pulled him after the others. Miller and Schultz were seated on ornate chairs with horsehair padding on the seats and armrests. They had bottles of wine and glasses and were talking loudly in English to the Italians who surrounded them. Moore was shoved into a similar chair and the girl, laughing, sat in his lap. She tilted another glass to his lips and he drank, fighting for breath, afraid to touch her without being able to see what he was doing. When the glass was empty she got up and went away.

Miller was singing, keeping time for himself by waving his wine bottle.

"Hoy Marie, hoy Marie," he chanted. "*Cuando bello ritorno aqui.*"

"My God!" shouted Schultz. "Listen to the boy! What is it, Miller, yiddish?"

Moore pushed away several hands which offered him wine bottles and bent toward Schultz.

"What's going on?" he demanded. "They act like they were nuts. Do you suppose it's a religious festival or something?" and he looked around nervously, frowning and shaking his head at the smiling faces which surrounded them.

I knew it, thought Schultz. It's beginning already.

"It's a party," he said. "They love us, by God!" and he wrapped his arm around a girl who stood near him and looked up at her, giggling. Tilting his wine bottle carefully, he poured a thin red stream onto her bare feet. The wine ran in quick little rivulets through the dirt on the girl's feet and she laughed as though Schultz had tickled her armpits.

Moore looked away with a groan of disgust. Do other people find themselves saddled with ridiculous, idiotic things the way I do? Is it even possible that someone once found himself with two men like these, in a country like this one, hot, smelly, and foreign, a nightmare day and night, and that thing up north there, being somehow made worse and worse by the two men. Defiant, but of nothing, resenting me more than they resent the ones on the other side. Why aren't we countrymen instead of arguers and liars, behaving like lunatics, why can't they let it all go and settle for just that one thing, that one feeling? Surely that's important enough by itself, you wouldn't need anything else. And in the meantime what will we tell the captain? He's probably leaving the CP right now, with that smart-alec hillbilly driver of his, coming down to check up on us, and everything just lying there, airplanes, radios, maps, even the machine gun on the halftrack right where anybody could walk off with it. This is crazy, it's impossible, what will we tell him? It isn't just a party, it doesn't feel like that. Right in the middle of the afternoon? It's more than that, they're expecting something, they're too excited, and he looked with distaste at the happy, sweating, mobile faces around him. It's abnormal, he thought, and he went to Schultz and seized his arm.

"Listen," he said in Schultz's ear. "Let's get out of here, there's still time, there's something the matter with these people, there's something wrong . . ."

Schultz hiccupped and made a sour face.

"This stuff is green as hell," he said. "It's like that African rotgut."

Moore pushed his face closer to Schultz's ear, so close he could smell sweat and oily skin.

"Suppose they've all got typhus or something?" he said, trying to sound reasonable. He felt fingers plucking at his collar and whirled around.

"Damn it, get away!" he screamed at a boy behind him. "There's something going on, I tell you," he said in Schultz's ear. "They don't act this way every day, I've never seen any of them drunk before. It's almost like the Middle Ages, you remember, the tarantella or whatever it was . . ."

"Oh, for God's sake, why don't you have a drink or something," Schultz said. "Everybody's just having a good time, that's all. I told you what the old man said, it's a barbecue or some damn thing."

Moore shoved him viciously, almost pushing him from his ornate chair.

"Barbecue!" he shouted. "You're as bad as Miller. These people never heard of a barbecue! That wasn't what he meant and you know it! It's mixed up somewhere . . ."

"Then go ask the old bastard!" Schultz cried, recovering from the surprise of Moore's push. "You worry too much, you always have!"

Moore tried a sneer, staring at the back of the mechanic's sweaty neck, feeling too conspicuous in front of the Italians.

He went back to his chair and sat down in it. The Italians chattered and laughed, they waved bottles at each other and offered them to him, they enjoyed themselves. The scene reminded him of a photograph in the *National Geographic* magazine, so long ago, in his father's dim study on the second floor, where the light was always bad and the room used less and less until they had stored magazines and old toys and hats in it, a picture of a group of wild, scarred African tribesmen capering around a ridiculous throne, a throne made from a battered old shoeshine stand, with cracked, imitation leather seats and pitted brass supports for the shod feet which were thousands of miles away, supporting now a horny, impudent black foot covered with clay, dung and ashes, elongated and flat, corded like a frog's foot . . .

The girl who had spilled the wine on him came back. She was carrying a full wine bottle and a heavy, smeared glass which she thrust into his protesting hands. He shook his head vigorously, no, exaggerating the movement, trying to make her understand. He bent over and placed the bottle and the glass on the hard earth by his chair, but she immediately retrieved them and placed them in his hands again. He put them down and she put them back in his lap. He jumped at the touch of the heavy bottle, then seized it by the neck to prevent it from rolling from his knees to the ground. The girl giggled and pulled the cork.

"Stop it," he said to her, "can't you leave me alone? I don't want it, it's too hot . . ." but she was lifting his arm again, pushing the bottle to his mouth and, unable to halt the bottle without violence, he allowed it to clink against his teeth and then was drinking from the green bottle, thinking, it's probably cleaner than the glass, anyway.

He took the bottle from his mouth, from her hand, and placed it on the ground. There were cries of approval from the people standing around his chair. They drank from their bottles too, and made encouraging signs to him with their free hands.

"Oh, lordy," he said, feeling the wine burn in his churning stomach, "what's going on here, anyway . . ."

The girl sat in his lap and started unbuttoning the top of his coveralls but he pushed her away roughly and sat limp and hot in his horsehair chair. She came back with the bottle, making him drink from it again, and then again, until he pushed her away.

"I'd like to get this straightened out," he said to the crowd, and then he belched . . .

And what was the name of the boy who burped at the party? They were all in the sixth grade then and it was one of the kids who lived out of town a way, a farm boy, really, since he lived too close to town for them to call it a ranch. A farm was all right, too, if your father didn't do the work himself, and there were riding horses. That's what the others thought but I didn't. It was Dorothy's party, the first organized, announced party he had ever attended, he remembered, with Japanese lanterns in the back yard. She lived over near the entrance to Cameron park, and the terrible thing happened in the dining room, where Dorothy's mother had herded everybody, drinking the dark, sickly grape punch. The boy who lived outside of town had belched as they stood there in their party clothes, a great, ripping, farmyard belch which sounded like a grown man, and they had stood, rigid with horror. I thought I would die, just feel a terrible squeezing pain in my stomach and die, I was so embarrassed.

"Grape jelly always makes me belch," the farm boy said, and he smiled gently at Dorothy's mother.

The girls screamed with laughter then, and the boys guffawed and snorted, making fun of him, but the farm boy kept his quiet smile, not embarrassed at all. I went outside, it was cool on the grass, shaking with shame and afraid I would be sick, which would be the worst thing, worse than the belch. I thought they would hold it against me, as though he were my best friend, or a relative, and that would be terrible, I wanted everybody to like me, and I think they did . . . but they would despise the belcher's friends! I hardly knew him, but for a long time I thought I would be blamed for it. How long did I go around worrying about it? . . .

He felt a bubble of gas form in his stomach and rise in his throat. He tried to check it, and hiccupped.

The crowd laughed, they liked him now, because he was drinking their wine after all. I don't care, he thought, I don't care whether you do or not and it's terrible stuff, and he looked at the bottle. It was almost empty, so he accepted another.

Now the old man, the particular old man, came out of the crowd in front of Schultz. He looked happier than before, as though something difficult and uncertain had been accomplished.

"She is here!" he shouted in Italian, and smiled at Schultz.

The crowd became more excited, it gathered itself and began moving away from the Americans, toward the other end of the farmyard.

The old man stood on tiptoe in front of the three sergeants, shouting at them and waving his hands toward the retreating crowd.

"Tell him to buzz off," Miller said sleepily. He was slouched in his chair with his eyes closed. The ground around him was littered with bottles, some of them still full.

Schultz stood up. "He wants us to follow the mob," he said. "Must be time to eat."

Moore's chair leaped away from him and flipped over on its back as he got to his feet. He frowned at it, then stared at the old man, squinting his eyes as though they hurt.

"Let's get out of here," he said. "Let's go back where we belong."

Miller sat up, brightening at the sound of Moore's voice.

"Where's that?" he said happily. "Where the hell do you think that is? Is there a saloon you know of around here?"

He stood up and began jogging around on his feet, almost shadow boxing, not looking at Moore.

"I think that's a damn good idea," he said in his high, happy voice. "That's the first sensible thing I heard since I cashed in my PX checks. Let's go back where we belong!"

"Shut up," Moore said. "Shut up shut up shut up."

The old man nodded quickly at Miller and seized his arm. The sergeant folded the little Italian in his arms and began an exaggerated waltz with him in the heat of the farmyard.

"Mother of God," said the old man, his voice muffled against Miller's chest, his left arm extended rigidly, his left hand in Miller's hand, his right hand involuntarily on the sergeant's shoulder.

"*Hoy Marie!*" yelled Miller. "*Hoy Marieeee!*"

Timidly, fearful of offending the sergeant, the old man tried to pull away from his partner, but Miller held him more tightly and continued his scraping and stumbling on the beaten earth.

"*Hoy Marie! Hoy Marie!*" he shouted. "*Cuando bello ritorno aqui!*"

"What's he saying?" the old man cried in Italian, twisting his neck, trying to look at Moore or Schultz. "Is this the way of things in New York, friends?"

Miller released him suddenly and sat down hard on the ground. He watched the old man run tiptoeing to the gate and disappear beyond it.

"Nothing's any damn good in this country," he said sadly. "A bunch of pallbearers."

"You're the corpse," Schultz said. "You and Moore, you're the corpse. They're going to put you birds in one of those fancy black wagons with the big plate glass windows, like they have in Naples, with silver trimmings all over, and haul you down that lonesome road. I feel sorry for you, boy," the mechanic said, looking intently at Miller. "It makes me sad to think about it." He drank from his bottle and then cradled it carefully on his knees and looked sadly at Miller.

"You're a good boy, Miller," he said. "You're kind of a jerk sometimes but you're a good boy, you poor, motherless orphan, you. You just never had any education, that's all that's wrong with you, Miller. That and the fact that the army got you too soon and the CCC's before that and your aunt owns that silly damned business in Illinois—what is it again?"

"They make cosmetics for mortuaries," Miller said, sitting on the ground with his arms around his knees and his chin on his arms.

"That's it," Schultz said after taking another drink. "Vanishing cream for the stiffs. I knew it was something that nutty but I couldn't think of it for a minute. Lipstick and rouge and powder and mascara for the departed, by God. It's something to think about, all right. It's essential. I'll bet they don't even slap a luxury tax on that stuff. I've thought about it ever since you first told me. I can't get it out of my mind. I can't figure out how they ever thought it up, it's so wonderful. Do you suppose the relatives of the departed insisted upon it, or did some smart cookie of a mortician think of it? To begin with, I mean. How does an idea like that get around, that's what I'd like to know. And the hell of it is," he said slowly, "you can't get a damn thing out of those morticians!"

He pounded his fist angrily on his thigh, but not too angrily, being careful about the wine bottle.

"They're a close-mouthed bunch!" he cried indignantly. "Yes, sir! They'd never tell you how a thing like that got started, oh, no. Bunch of buttonmouths, think they have ethics, for Christ's sakes!

Let me tell you, Miller," and he looked fondly at Miller, looking at him as a father would look, "I've had dealings with those people. There was a time in my life when they fascinated me, like to drove me nuts. I was practically queer on the subject. I pestered the life out of the morticians in St. Louis until they took to calling up my father and asking him to keep me away. I wanted to know! that's all it was, I just wanted to know what the hell went on down there, but those jerks wouldn't let me in on the secret."

He pulled the slippery scarf from around his neck, trailing it into his lap and onto the ground. When he mopped the sweat from his face the scarf came away gray and dingy. He continued to talk, like one scientist to another, telling of his difficulties on a research project.

"It wasn't that I never got *in*," he said to Miller, who had found a bottle and was staring sadly at it. "I got *in*, all right. You can always get in, through the door from the alley, a window in summertime, even through the front door, when nobody's looking. And even if they are, what the hell, they haven't got anything to hide, have they? But God damn it," he said with exasperation, "the stiffs were always gone! They always sneaked them out just before I got there or locked them up or some damn thing. They were there in the *caskets*, of course," he said, raising his hands quickly as though to stop a remark from Miller, "I often saw them lying down in their quilted satin boxes, they looked like they'd been carved out of Ivory soap and painted with cheap watercolors, like they'd been Pranged, which of course they had, but," and he spaced his words carefully and distinctly as though this were the crux of his speech, "they were never on the slabs."

He drained the last wine from his bottle and threw it away.

"Why don't you shut up," said Moore from his chair. "Those people have all gone so why don't you shut up?"

He stared at Schultz, working his eyebrows up and down, trying to focus his glare.

Schultz rose and walked over to a full wine bottle, took it by the neck and returned to his seat. His movements were brisk and purposeful. He looked like a well-adjusted businessman now, happily discussing some problem of buttons or wholesale shoes, certain the problem would be solved in time, hugging himself to himself, delighted with what he was. He ignored Moore.

"I won't say my curiosity is as strong now as it was then," he said, after frowning thoughtfully at Miller. "I can really take a corpse or leave it alone, nowadays, unless it's someone I know, of course. Then I don't want to have anything to do with it. The trouble, and the uproar! Really, you can't beat a good civilian murder, that's the best kind. It's more interesting, more personal than this crap over here. In civilian life a murder makes you squirm a little bit, you figure, what the hell, that might have been me, on one side or the other, either killer or victim, and it gives you something to think about for a few hours, or minutes, anyway.

"I got in on a good murder once, in a little burg outside of East St. Louis. I went with a pal of mine who was a reporter on the *Post-Dispatch*, but he didn't last long there. I wonder whatever happened to him? Anyway, this farmer had hit his wife on the head with the blunt end of an axe and then shot her through the left tit with a revolver. I may have the sequence reversed there, but I don't think it makes a hell of a lot of difference. The local undertaker had her in a wire basket next to his radiator, trying to thaw her out when we got there. She'd been lying in the house about a week in the wintertime with no heat, you know, and she was a real stiff. The undertaker was drunk and so was his wife, damndest thing you ever saw, and while he talked to us he leaned on an old shriveled-up grandmother, naked as a jay bird. 'I think she's softened up a bit,' he'd say, and he'd toddle over and shove on the victim's bare belly. We all had several drinks and before it was all over we all had a good shove at her, both on the stomach and the skull, which was busted like a cracked coconut and squeaked when you pushed on it. A hell of a thing. All the undertaker's kids were in and out of the room all night and I kept noticing they all wore a little gold charm around their necks on a string, like a church medal, and when I finally got hold of one and took a good look it was a little gold barrel, like you get on Seagram's gin, the yellow kind.

"I haven't thought of that in years," he said, looking fondly at Miller. "You must have reminded me of it, you and Moore in that black coach with the silver trimming and your loveable old aunt in Illinois. Do you think you could get me a job with her outfit after the war? Maybe I could be the falsies representative. Schultz's Pneumatic Boobs for Concave-Chested Cadavers. What a franchise for some town in Kansas, southwestern Kansas would be a good spot for that, or even Omaha. Listen!" he cried excitedly to Miller. "Have they ever thought of that? You could even have shoulder pads for the male stiffs, see, well-made ones out of sponge rubber, maybe come in five, six sizes, fit anybody, or excuse me, boy, fit anyone."

"Will you please shut up," Moore said. His eyes were closed and he sagged in his chair, about to fall out of it. Schultz looked at him angrily.

"Just because you're going to be buried in a mattress cover, don't think everybody else is," he said. "This is a hell of a thing we've run across here. Of course I can understand why you and maybe even Miller maybe don't see it like I do because you won't be around to enjoy the fruits of this wonderful, wonderful idea. Even in a depression people have to be buried, don't you get it? Even if you're on the WPA or in the CCC's like poor old Miller boy here, you have to be buried, for Christ's sake! Cradle to the grave, the Government will pay for it, they'll pay for anything. What do you think those mattress covers cost? Good canvas, tight stitching by some horny-handed girl in Waco, Texas, hell, you could get twenty dollars for one in Africa, remember? That's good stuff you and Miller are going to be bundled up in, riding in that black and silver coach, winding down the road from Capodichino with the stragglers in black strung out behind. Remember that, Miller? Remember the coach, on the road down from Capodichino, the last time we went down for a bath? They even had a couple of horses, Moore, I wish you could have seen it. The most piddly-assed funeral I ever saw in my life, looked like the whole works was going to bust down any minute right in the road and roll the casket into the ditch. They tell me they use those caskets over and over again, just part of the dressing to get you out to the cemetery, that's all. I'm afraid they won't even change that for you boys, although you're their liberators and their glorious allies and you fly the little birds and holler into the little radio and I don't know what all. No caskets, not even for you. You can use it for the ride, but after that it's just the old mattress cover. It would be quite a thing, though, at that, if we could get the Italians to run it," he said, and he smiled at Miller, then at Moore. "They've probably never handled a GI funeral in one of those coaches and I'll bet there'd be a hell of an uproar, the Goddamned Italians would all want to get into the act and too many would and they'd probably drop you both before they got you loaded, drop your stitched-up mattress covers right in the street. And then some bird, a skinny fellow probably with a mustache and a tight black suit, all dressed up for your sakes, he'll take out a piece of chalk the Germans left in the post office or someplace, some little piece they overlooked, and he'll write on the sides of the coach, *'Viva Americani!'* or something like that and off you'll go, on your way to the marble orchard. You know, I'm out of vino."

"Under your chair," Miller said.

I'm surprised Moore didn't bust out crying, thought Schultz, reaching for the bottle. I thought I put it plainly enough, but he must not be tuned in, I'll have to keep scratching around on his crystal. What'll I tell him about, Woodrow Wilson? The Woodrow Wilson Post of the Veterans of by God Foreign by God Wars or the Woodrow Wilson they talk about out at the veterans' home near Leavenworth? Where they stand out on the porch all day long, with their belts knotted in their fists, lashing at the pillars, calling Woodrow Wilson every dirty name they can think of. But of course those guys are screwy, they think they've got Woodrow strung up there, they don't know he gave them the slip and that's nothing but red bricks and cement, if it hasn't fallen down by now, and for Moore you have to make it sound normal, he's afraid of anything else. Even queers wear galoshes, Moore! I wish I could tell him that, but he wouldn't know what I was talking about, he's never been in the Wichita bus station at three in the morning. The saddest place in the world, they'll have a mass suicide there some day, there won't be anybody left but the ticket seller and the shine boy and the cabbies, waiting for the three-fifteen from Junction City or Medicine Lodge or wherever they come from at that time, maybe nowhere. I can't think of anyplace where anybody would deliberately fix it so they were going to arrive at that station at three-fifteen a.m. Maybe the buses are all empty, pounding down the bricks on Highway Eighty-one, coming in from Newton and Valley Center and Emporia, empty, with nothing aboard but the drivers and bundles of the *Kansas City Times,* as if they didn't have enough newspapers in the damned town already. The Boy Scouts make Mummy take the paper so they can fill up the basement with trash and make a good showing on Paper Day. The smart kids load their bundles with tire irons and jack handles, when they aren't using them to break into parked cars. Getting ahead! In a few years we'll have them over here with us, they're here already, in fact, and they still get the papers from home! Yes, sir! We get all the news from home: the head red cap at the depot retires after forty-five years of loyal, backbreaking labor and we know all about it, we know he got the gold watch, we know what he said, all together now, "I just want to relax and do a little fishing." That's it. In three years he'll be dead, and no fish, the fish don't give a shit for him or anybody else, and why should they? He can take his Pflueger and go pflueg himself with it. And we'll all remember what he told the pimple-faced jerk from the *Times*: "Why, no, nothing unusual has ever happened to me in my forty-five years of service for the Kansas City Terminal Railway Company, nothing at all . . ." And of course it hasn't, Jack, just lust, robbery, adultery, sodomy and other assorted shenanigans, worn-out souls flaring into cinders like skyrockets right in front of his placid red cap's eyes. But it isn't unusual! He's right! He didn't want to bother the readers with a lot of piddling crap they knew about already, and he's right, they're sick of it.

You want to hear about that, Moore? You want to hear what they'd do to you if you ever got back? What'll it be, the Wichita bus station on the dogwatch with all the fags painted up, waiting for something, something, anything, "a climax," one of them said. Or do you want to wait for your climax in the railroad station, or the First National Bank, or in the universal Men's Room, developing hemorrhoids while you try to kill a little time. Actually, they don't know what a break they're getting, the Moores of this world don't. They don't realize how wonderful everything really is, so much better than even that splendid idea they have of it. Why should Moore worry about all that stuff that worried me. He's young, he has good eyesight and no hemorrhoids, so sooner or later one of those eighty-eights will connect, it happens every day, or maybe even a forty millimeter, or a twenty, or even a rifle bullet, they can reach you easy at three thousand feet. Or, if you're real lucky, if you'd like to make Ernie Pyle's column, maybe you'll get hit by one of our own shells, one you've just asked for over the radio. That happens, too, but not so often that it's stale news, it's still an item for Ernie and the other blood-suckers . . .

Lots of times you can feel them, Miller had said. Bumpety bump, right underneath, when they let go a lot of them at once it's like a lot of real hard downdrafts, one right after the other.

Some guy at corps got his prop hit, it didn't go off, just smeared gray paint on the blade and busted it all to hell. A smoke shell, that gray paint is on the smoke shells, Miller had said.

Ah, yes, thought Schultz: and what's on the others, a stenciled greeting from the commander in chief? Pull in your balls, squeeze your asshole tight, put your head between your knees, here it is! from yours truly, FDR. Maybe I am getting old, at that.

"You know, I'm thirty-eight years old," he said.

"Oh, for Christ's sakes!" Miller drank from his bottle and looked bored.

"It's different for you birds," Schultz went on. "My feet hurt me all the time. You know I never even finished a hike at Sill. I should never have been in the Army at all, and now you think I'm a jerk."

He blew his nose on his scarf.

"You are," Moore said, not opening his eyes. "You're a jerk."

Moore wanted to move from the chair, to leave the farmyard and return to the tent, but he felt dizzy and sick. If he moved he would vomit, and he had always hated to vomit, even at home where he could go and lie on the cool sheets of his bed afterward. Here, in the heat and foreign smell, it would be terrible. I won't do it, he thought. I'll hold it in, like I did so many times at school when I was a kid, moving as little as possible, not moving at all.

Never mind Schultz and his coach and his mattress covers, we should get back to the line, it's really better there, somehow . . . the fine feeling when everything is going well, like hunting. And you had to be clever, too, you had to think ahead of the guns, some people were good at it and others weren't, you had to think yourself into the frightened truck driver or the motorcyclist, although it was always best to wait until the motorcycle stopped at a house, or in a grove of trees. That usually meant a headquarters of some sort. And you had to see the muzzle flash in that one instant when it stabbed orange in the gray and mark it exactly, like sticking a pin into a detailed map. And shifting the bursts: if you could make a four hundred yard shift and get on they didn't have a chance, it was there in the split second when they first heard it coming, and right behind it, in the same aerial groove, six more coming, all in the air at once, before the first of the six burst. We have wonderful gunners, he thought, excellent, they're a thousand times more important than Schultz and Miller. And then he heard the crowd coming back through the gate.

[x] The Italians were shouting, and in their midst was a large white animal which they were leading on a rope and urging from behind with cries and blows.

"My God," said Schultz, "here comes our barbecue. It's still alive."

The animal was a white cow, a sad-looking animal whose skin hung in flapping folds around its neck and from its leg joints. Despite the tattoo of sticks on its rump and the shouts of the crowd it came slowly and calmly toward the sergeants.

Oh, no, thought Moore. My Lord, no. Are they going to kill that thing right here and eat it?

"Fresh meat," cried Schultz. "On the table, not the altar, that's right. Where's the french fries?"

He stood up, rocking a little, and went forward to meet the cow. Miller followed, doing his little dancing shuffle.

"How long does it take to barbecue something?" Miller said, very happy. "They won't be able to get that thing done tonight, will they? I could eat a horse!"

"You're close, boy, very close," Schultz said, patting the cow's neck. "A fugitive from Chicago! The race is not always to the Swifts!"

He turned to the Italians and made eating motions. "When?" he said in their language. "When eat?"

"No, no!" they shouted, laughing. *"Niente mangiare!"* and they made signs with their hands for something else and said it in Italian.

"My God!" cried Schultz.

"What is it?" said Miller, impatient. "What did they say?"

"Didn't you see them?" said Schultz. "Didn't you see what they did?" and he did it with his hands.

"Us?" said Miller, his sleepy eyes widening. "They mean us?" and he jiggled frenziedly in his dance. "I never tried screwing a cow before."

Schultz shook his head.

"No," he said, "and it kind of worries me a little. I think we'd come out of this better if at least one of us had. These people are really something now, aren't they? Anything for the by God Americani, that's their motto," and he patted the cow affectionately and smiled at the people around him.

Miller hopped rapidly on one foot and then the other, his fists jerking out in quick punching movements. He thought it unlikely that Schultz's diagnosis was correct but he found the idea interesting and was busily going over it in his mind, changing and fitting the images together as best he could, trying to work out the details.

"You never know about people," Schultz said, smiling at a man who gave him a bottle of wine. "I'll admit it seems a little queer when you first think of it, but what the hell, I suppose we've all heard of things like that, haven't we? Reminds me of a hunchbacked girl used to come in the Hotel Muehlebach in Kansas City, and you always want to remember it's the Hotel Muehlebach, not the Muehlebach Hotel, there's a hell of a difference. This girl was a mess, a regular mistake, she sold flowers in the bar there, but she got knocked up by an ex-prize fighter who hung around Twelfth and Baltimore, carried his money in his shoe, clear inside his sock, so he wouldn't have to buy drinks for anybody. He didn't, either, all the bartenders knew where the money was and they didn't want any part of it. They used to pee in his whiskey occasionally, he was such a no good bastard, but they wouldn't let him buy anybody a drink. The arrangement suited him fine, sort of taking the bitter with the sweet, you might say, arf and arf. Well, what I'm getting at is nobody but that guy could have gotten that girl pregnant, it wouldn't have occurred to anybody else, he was a real screwy looey. In a way, it's the same thing with this cow here."

Moore made a choking sound and wine gushed from his mouth, wetting his clothes before he could bend over. Then he leaned forward, too late, swaying in misery as a trickle of wine and saliva rolled down his chin, his neck and disappeared under his coveralls.

I want to lie down, he thought, I want to go back, go back, and he felt himself falling, unable to put out his hands, and hit the dirt hard, the jar making him breathless. His stomach jumped in spasms and he retched again, lying on the ground.

I have to go home, he thought, I can't tell the teacher or anybody, I just have to go home before I do it again out in the hall and somebody sees me.

But he was not home, and after a while he sat up carefully, supporting himself with his arms stiff and quivering, staring at the group in the farmyard, at the cow.

"He's back, fellows!" yelled Schultz. "There goes Ole Thirteen, back into the game! Just a little Charleyhorse, that's all it was, after all. Boy!" he cried, looking wildly around. "Boy!" he called, and bent over to look under the placid cow's belly. The movement was too quick and he fell to his knees. Rising quickly and briskly, dusting his trousers, he ignored his tumble. "Oh, there you are!" he shouted, seizing Miller by the arm. "Here, boy, get this out to Ole Thirteen right away. Don't let him swallow any, just rinse his mouth with it!" and he handed Miller a half-empty wine bottle.

"The cup that cheers," Miller said sadly and drank from the bottle, not moving toward Moore.

"It does, of course it does!" said Schultz. He leaned back against the cow's flank, throwing his left arm up to lie on her back as on a fireplace mantel. He stood there like the genial host in front of his fireplace, smiling and bobbing his head up and down at Miller, the guest, agreeing with this transient visitor.

"I've often thought of that," he said, nodding as though he had not heard Miller say this a thousand times.

"Past regrets and future fears," Miller said, looking at Schultz with his sleepy eyes.

"It's the little things that count in this world and don't you ever forget it."

A group of men appeared in the gate, running forward and then back, leading a large white bull into the farmyard with a rope. The bull snorted and swung his head, holding it low, trying to hook with his horns in a halfhearted way. He advanced with quick little running steps, then halted, tugging gently against the rope which was tied to a ring in his nose. The Italians jerked on the rope and he trotted forward again, protesting.

The cow moved suddenly, nervously, and the bull seemed to see her for the first time. He halted, stared at her, then raised his head in a bawling bellow.

"What in the world," said Moore from his seat on the ground. Still dizzy from the wine and vomiting, he looked at the scene in the farmyard without understanding it. Miller was jiggling in his little dance, Schultz was slapping the cow on her back and the Italians were capering around the two animals, shouting at each other. More Italians came running in through the gate, carrying baskets filled with wine bottles. The bull came easily and steadily now, paying no attention to the shouting Italians, his eyes fixed on the skittish cow.

"Hey," Moore called, trying to get up. "Hey, somebody head him off! Wave something at him!"

"It's waving, it's waving!" shouted Schultz, and he slapped the cow's rump. "He sees it, Moore, don't get excited! We've got everything under control over here!"

I knew it, thought Moore. All the filth, all the blood and spit and dung are coming out now, and he managed to get to his feet.

He stood there, holding his arms slightly away from his body to steady himself, watching the bull move toward the cow.

"Don't let him!" he called weakly, but no one paid any attention. Schultz had run forward to meet the bull and was trotting along beside the great, rolling bulk, uttering cries of encouragement. At a safe distance Miller jogged happily up and down, his arms shooting out spasmodically.

Moore was terrified, and for some reason which he had no time to understand he knew the bull must not reach the cow. He moved, he tried to run, but his legs refused him and he fell dizzily after stumbling a few steps. Drunkenness washed over him in waves, coming and going, echoing in his ears, and he watched the bull, like a slow-motion film, the bull throwing himself back on his hind legs, rearing and trembling a moment before he plunged forward.

Moore's despairing cry was lost in the shouts of the Italians. As the bull reared their voices slid up the scale, then fell as the animal dropped from the cow's back and stood on his four legs again. Their voices were low and sad as they stood looking at the bull.

"He missed!" cried Schultz. "A nervous groom, did you see that, Moore?"

This is terrible, thought Moore, I can't watch anything like that. These people are crazy, getting us over here to watch a thing like that, for he realized now the old man had meant this. Schultz and his barbecue! A hot, prickly feeling swept over Moore's body as he looked at the bull and then away.

The bull swung his head nervously from side to side, annoyed by the people crowding around him, and his feet shuffled rapidly and dangerously in the dirt. Suddenly he reared again and crashed onto the cow, hopping grotesquely to reach her. The Italians shouted.

"aaaaAAH!" they said as the bull went up, then, "AAaaah," diminishing, as he came back to earth, unfulfilled.

Moore sat down in his chair.

"I'd like to have the whole Fifth Army see this," Schultz said, walking over and sitting in the other chair. "Including Mock Clock, sitting right here in the grandstand. All except the English, of course. They wouldn't know what the hell was going on."

The bull, thought Moore. The bull was a failure, a flop, he was ridiculous, worse than useless, because it takes something to feed him. These people! Whatever they do, whichever way they turn, it's wrong, it doesn't come out right. A bull, like that . . .

"I've never liked bulls," he said, and he leaned his head back against the chair, breathing heavily with his mouth open.

"Really?" Schultz looked at Moore's closed eyes, smiling. "They're usually more effective than this, I think, at that. What the hell, they're designed for the job, they don't have anything to worry about. These people, though, they're really something, aren't they? We're the guests of honor at a breeding party, you know, unless you count the bull and the cow, and if it turns out to be a breeding party as scheduled. They've all had a lot of faith in that bull, probably for years by the looks of him, really counted on him. And why not? What the hell can you count on, if not a bull? Not a damn thing, especially in this bare-assed country they've got here. Now they find out even the bull is no damn good. It's enough to make you think, isn't it?"

A fly buzzed about Moore's face, attracted by his open mouth but frightened by his breathing.

Schultz took a deep, gulping drink from his bottle and looked at Moore.

"Maybe it all means something," he said, waving a hand listlessly, vaguely. "Don't you like to think it does? Don't you like to think it all has some kind of order, some reason behind it, like it was all laid out in a book of rules somewhere? But hell," he shouted angrily, "they use a worm for a bookmark!"

Moore laughed and fell back into his chair.

"I know how you feel," Schultz said soothingly. "Don't you

think I feel the same way, really? What I was saying a minute ago about dying, it sounded silly, didn't it? Can you imagine being killed now? I can't think of anything more unlikely, even for you and Miller," he said, and he sounded content. "It's fantastic, you know it? Here we are, thousands of us over here and thousands of them over there, and people dying every day, killing each other! Ha! I don't believe it! I can see the bull, the poor old broken-down bull, but I can't see the rest. Really, it's too screwy. The only thing that bothers me," he said confidentially to Moore, who sat with his head in his hands, "is the shelling. I've been meaning to ask you if we can't pick a strip in a better place this time."

Moore did not answer, and after waiting a moment Schultz leaned back in his chair and smiled at the crowd around the bull. He watched Miller dancing around the group, urging the Italians to do something.

"After all, we're not in the infantry, you know," Schultz said, watching Miller. "There's no point in making it tougher than it is."

"We!" Moore raised his head and stared at the mechanic.

"I know," said Schultz. "I'm a son of a bitch."

"Listen!" said Moore. "Why don't you get up there with nothing but a stove lid under your seat? You've never looked over your shoulder at a red-nosed Messerschmidt, or flown through a burst! Just tell me, have you ever known that everybody in the world was trying to get you, *you,* damn you!"

"I know," said Schultz.

"No, you don't know!" Moore said viciously. "You're filthy, Schultz! You don't know anything and you don't believe anything and you make fun of everybody who does, and I'm sick of it! Why can't you let me alone, I'm not like you. You act like it was all a big joke, being here and being in the Army, as though somebody was playing a trick on us, as though there weren't any war or anything bad about it. Why is it, Schultz?" he said, and he was crying now, loudly, as he had not cried since he was a child, "is it because you're thirty-eight years old?"

"Ah, listen," said Schultz.

"Well, I'm twenty-one years old!" said Moore. "And I know why I'm here, I know nobody's playing a trick on me!" and the tears ran down his face, leaving streaks in the dirt. "I know what you think," he said, "you think I'll never go home again, don't you, you don't believe in anything, anything. Well, I do! Anyway," he said after a pause, "the war won't last forever, you know."

"Of course it won't," said Schultz.

"You're a liar," Moore said, and pressed his hands to his eyes. "Leave me alone."

"Now listen," Schultz began, but Moore stopped him.

"Go on, greaseball," he said with his hands over his eyes. "Leave me alone, loudmouth."

"I'm sorry," Schultz said, and he got up and walked over to the Italians, the animals, and Miller.

"He can't get his pecker up," Miller said as Schultz came over to him. "They tried everything, they even tickled him with a stick, but it didn't do any good. Isn't that a hell of a fix to be in?"

"Terrible," said Schultz.

"What's the matter now?" asked Miller, looking from Schultz to Moore, hunched in his chair.

"I think he's blowing his top," Schultz said. "He's not taking the proper view of all this."

"What do you mean? This steer here, and the cow?" Miller lowered his wine bottle in surprise. "What view is that?"

"Oh, I don't know," the mechanic said, irritated. "I just said it. And it's not a steer, it's a bull."

"I suppose he's pissed off again," Miller said happily. "I suppose cows and steers don't act like this in Texas, is that it now?"

"Miller," said Schultz. "Tell me something."

"Well?" Miller stared at the mechanic, waiting for him to continue.

"Never mind," said Schultz.

Are you afraid, I wanted to ask him, are you afraid up there, thought Schultz, but you can't do that, I suppose. It wouldn't accomplish anything, in fact it's unheard of, everything would go all to hell if you started that kind of thing. I'm afraid of it, terribly afraid of it, me, on the ground, almost out of range, and Moore knows it's there, but Miller doesn't even understand it. He understands a bum rap and a dirty deal, but he doesn't understand that. Do you suppose he thinks he could goldbrick his way out of that, too? No, he doesn't think about it at all . . . he's still on maneuvers someplace, thinking that any day now they'll quit this silliness and go back into barracks. Hell, you can get *hurt* out here! that's what he thinks . . .

"How about some poetry, Miller," he said, smiling.

"In Exandoo did Kooblah Can a stately pleasuredom degree," recited Miller, striking a dramatic pose, one hand on his breast and the other dangling from his outflung arm. "Where Alf the sacred river ran through taverns measureless to man down to a sunless sea . . ."

"That's the stuff," Schultz said, taking a wine bottle from a smiling Italian. "That's the stuff, *paesan.*"

[IX]   How sad, thought Schultz, everybody will be dead but me. He smiled at the people standing around him and at the bull moving nervously at the end of the rope. Dimly he heard Miller's voice reciting, but he paid no attention, slowly lowering himself to the ground, allowing his legs to fold, holding the wine bottle delicately by the neck.

I should have told Moore, he thought. Moore, I should have said, maybe a thousand years from now some GI will dig a shit trench in your grave and never know the difference. You've probably dug up a Roman or Etruscan yourself and hidden your droppings in his hole. That's life, Moore! that's what I should have said. It's sad, everything's sad, but that's the way it is. You can think of anything, anything at all, and if you think about it long enough it's sad as hell. *Triste.* No bloody good. Even the weather. A nice bright day in the fall, a cool feeling on the shadow side of everything but warm out in the sun. That's enough to twist your guts out, Moore! All the beautiful, fresh young women you saw go by on days like that, and you never spoke to them, never saw them again. Or the ones you did speak to, that you spent days like that with, that you made love to before you were thirty-eight years old. Where are they now? Where are the feeky-feeks of yesteryear, he said to himself, trying to be brutal, trying to fight the knowledge that he was drunk and dirty, sprawled in the filth of a nameless farmyard with grease under his fingernails, wearing last week's socks and underwear. We used to meet by the railroad bridge, not the one in town but out on the west, out where the trees grew so neatly along the river, with such order, and we'd walk along the Neckar on the towpath, watching the barges until we got to the restaurant, remember? And we always had the same table on the bricks, under the biggest tree, because you could look down the river from that table and everything tasted better there. Those winey afternoons, they don't have wine like that anymore, I'll bet, and I don't even remember the name of it. Maybe I couldn't even find the restaurant, but yes, I know I could do that, certainly. But it's probably moved, it sat there a hundred years and now if I want to find it again the bastards will have moved it, for no reason whatever. Well, the hell with them, there are other places to eat, you know, the country's full of places right along there, wonderful places . . .

And now she's probably standing in line at a water point somewhere, the skin on her bare legs cracked and purple, split, with sores on her ankles and a bucket on her arm, or maybe she's a whore in Mannheim, or Stuttgart, or Muenchen. Either that or the sweetie of some sergeant, maybe even an officer, walking with him somewhere or waiting for him to come back from Russia, from *der drang nach osten,* you betcha, the son of a bitch. Or maybe he's up there in the mountains, thinking about me. Maybe she told him about me and the poor bastard is squatting in a rock pile up there somewhere with his nose full of dust, thinking about me and about her, about how clean her hair smelled, only it probably doesn't smell that way now, after two or three years of sleeping in the *luftschutzkeller.* Besides, he thought with a little stab of shock, she must be thirty-five by now and nobody smells like that when they're thirty-five, and he inhaled deeply of his own odor there in the farmyard, the sweat and smell of his hot, greasy clothing and the animal fat smell from his clumsy boots. Nothing's worth a damn, he thought, with such sadness that it was almost a cool, safe and relaxed feeling. It's all politics, anyhow.

Like at Lucien's bar in Grenoble, he went on drunkenly, ignoring the buzz of the farmyard and Miller's sing-song voice, reciting. Those characters with the little red stars under their lapels, like you get on chewing tobacco, buying us drinks because we said we had been in Spain, for Christ's sake, and we'd never been near the damn country at all. And the ski politics, the one bunch parading around the Place Grenette in their rich clothing and the others in that little bar out on the edge of town toward Voirons, where you went up the mountain. If you felt honest you went out to the bar on the edge of town, but if you were thirsty you went to the Place Grenette and found somebody to drink with in Felix's, or someplace else where it was expensive. And I usually did that, I was usually thirsty, he told himself angrily, I was the same way even then, long before then. The hell of it was I could drink better with the Grenette crowd and their beautiful, well-fashioned women. You didn't have to think about anything but the drinks and the nice smells, there were even potato chips on the tables. But at the edge of town it was ski, ski, ski, until everybody was in

a fever from it, they all thought they were Greek heroes drinking
hot white wine at a penny a shot, everything was *en haut, en
haut!* until you were ready to climb the mountain right then and
there, ready to claw your way up the bastard with nothing on but
street shoes and a single-breasted suit, like the nigger who did and
died. The colored boy couldn't understand it, it drove him nuts, he
had to get up there and find out what the hell it was all about so
of course he froze to death when the liquor wore off. Whenever I
started feeling like that I went back to the Place Grenette, I went
back there and talked ski to those rich bastards until my tongue
was swollen like a sausage, and then I forgot it, so let's forget it
now. Anyway, they're all gone, I'll never see them again, not any
of it again, it's all thrown away like everything else. The house in
Heilbronn must be gone by now, it was a railroad town, you
know, they wouldn't have overlooked that, and of course I suppose
Berlin is finished completely. Everything's smashed, what the hell,
I always knew it would be, everywhere I went. There's nothing in
the other direction, either, it all stinks, it's rotten, worn out by the
crazy way they do things, rubbed right down until it screeches like
a slate, until all the stringy ugliness shows through. A million
square miles of Pittsburgh! That's all, cheap towns, crooks, thugs,
syphilitic sheep looking for a Judas goat every minute of their
lives, north or south, east or west, just asking for it! And they get
it, right where it does the most good, it's a broken bottle-end in
their kissers and they don't even feel it, they're as bugged as a
shack full of Mexicans, hopped up, floating, way up in the clouds,
it's raining urine and they think it's imported perfume, duty free,
the rivers are brimfull of stale piss. The secondhand paradise,
overnight everything's a junk heap with a brand-new billboard on
top, a tremendous advertisement for soap or oleomargarine. Junk,
junk, always more, the place is smothered in it! And what the hell
are we supposed to be up to? They'll have a new label for it
tomorrow or the next day, we'll hear about it, we get the home-
town papers, it'll all be explained. Don't you know what you stand

for, you slob? Don't you get it? For the love of motherhood, by the bylaws of the American Legion, by the sweet feet of Christ's sick self, don't you understand it? It's simple enough, we're doing our best to put up with you, you know, but don't try us too much or we're liable to drop you into the hot seat. Look, we have a flag, it's red, white and blue. We're religious, we practically have the racket sewed up, in fact, the next pope will probably be a New Yorker. We have a two-ocean navy and the Panama Canal, without one you wouldn't have the other and that's simple enough, isn't it? We have the Statue of Liberty, New York Harbor, WE SPEAK ENGLISH, FOR CHRIST'S SAKE! Are you nuts, or what? This is all yours, son, don't you get it? Some day it'll belong to you, you've got to understand that, you've got to live up to it, this didn't come about overnight, you know. It took a long time, a lot of sweat to get us where we are today, but if you keep acting the way you do you're liable to knock the whole works over, we might wind up with something else instead. And it wouldn't be any damned good, either, you can believe that, nothing else ever is. It starts out fine, we know that, but it all goes to hell in a hurry. You know that, admit it, come on now, it's silly to question the status quo, even to wonder about it, isn't it? . . . yes, yes, leave me alone, leave yourself alone, thought Schultz. I should explain all this to Moore but I don't give a good God damn, I know that nothing, not one single thing is worth anything at all except myself, because I'm alive, there isn't anything whatever beyond that, it's hooey, crap, the old con. It's thinking about Moore that does it, what started me off on it, anyway, I forgot all that stuff a long time ago. It was Moore and the bull. The bull failed, he's harmless to everybody now, you just have to sweat it out, that's all, and when it finally comes it's nothing at all, you're not afraid of it anymore. Money, the boss, a woman, none of it's as bad as you think it will be, not when it's finally on you, at your throat. Not if you know it isn't worth anything, that it's all so much crap, unimportant trash, the main thing is just yourself. Just thinking about myself in Heilbronn or Grenoble or Berlin is enough for me, I know you can't have anything more than that. I can think about the women, about the way they smelled and smiled and talked, the way they looked at me, their soft, warm thighs, beautiful kneecaps as delicate as watches, dimples in their hips, blonde fuzz in the hollows of shoulder blades, breasts burning and the feel of them through silk or cotton, that's enough. Or meals, drinks I had in a thousand places, sauerbraten, barbe-cued ribs, beer, chartreuse cardinals in Lucien's, alexanders in the morning at the Hotel Europe, fifteen-year-old scotch in the Coal Hole, hot frankfurters in Harry's Bar, or the barrels of beer at The Peanut, chilled, freezing, on those steamy afternoons, soaked with sweat and my fingers smelling of money, somebody else's money. The same old crowd every afternoon, just like me, disgusted, sick of it, hating to go home, refusing to think of it all beginning again in the morning. The Bosses scattered all over town that we cursed and spat on, examining every detail of their perfidiousness, their niggardliness, their absolutely incredible stupidity, dragging out details about them that really floored you, we were horrified at each other's terrible luck! There wasn't one in the bunch that you'd save from the worst possible death by lifting so much as a finger, we were astounded at such a collection of idiots. Where did they come from, we wondered, how had they managed to become so completely, hopelessly inhuman? They thought more of their collie dogs than they did of us, it was obvious, no question about it at all. A fine thing, the bastards! Those silly dogs, it seemed they all had one, inbred, filthy, crapping anywhere, lying in it, it was all over their rear ends all the time, we'd see them, noses like needles, they hated your guts, they didn't care if you lived or died, just like their owners. Really, it's a wonder we weren't all commies, only it wasn't that sort of place, The Peanut. In fact, it wasn't even that sort of town, we stayed pure. The only one who came close to it was the reporter when he joined the guild, undercover. That upset us! We weren't sure he could be trusted after that! Fortunately, he didn't give a shit whether we thought so or not, all he wanted was to get out of his own private hellhole and into the Nut, where he could rave and rant all he wanted. A good thing, too, we heard things about the scum we worked for that might have escaped us, otherwise. There's nothing like having a friend who works for that paper, any paper, especially if he's a boozer. And of course we all were in our little way, we were awash in beer, all afternoon and far into the night, swearing vengeance, threatening anything, anything at all against our employers, the people who kindly made it possible for us to drink beer. What a mess! Speeches, shouts, obscenities, women waiting in vain for us all over town, suppers ruined, we didn't care! We were at grips with the devil himself, we had our hands around his throat, he was drowning in beer, we were about to win out! Jesus, you can't just go home when things have reached that pitch. It gets so you never want to go home at all, you never want to get out of bed again. What's the use? There's nothing ahead but the same old grind, months, years of it, you could write the script for the rest of eternity, there aren't any surprises in it, no trick endings, unless you go in for crime or jump the rails some other way, and then you really are finished, that's the excuse they're looking for. You won't be missed, we're overpopulated as it is, even the war won't change that, although it has brightened everybody up considerably, given us a change. What the hell! They know what they're doing, they let us go right up to the explosion point and then pull a diversion, jab a safety valve into us and let out just enough hot air. When we're thoroughly tired of this and they know it we'll all go back and start building up pressure again . . . God! Dear, sweet God! and Schultz began to cry, sitting on the ground with the wine bottle between his knees.

[xii]   " 'But I was young and foolish, and now am full of tears,' " said Miller.

He stood in front of Schultz with a bottle in his left hand, his right arm extended in a languid, limp-wristed gesture. He smiled down at Schultz.

"Everybody on a crying jag," he said happily. "The gooks are gonna think we're all queers."

He sipped from his bottle and watched Schultz dab at his face with the scarf.

"That's some bull," he said. "The barbecue was a better idea."

"Yes," said Schultz, looking up, his face clean where the tears and scarf had washed and wiped away the dirt. "I must be drunk as a hoot owl."

"Don't worry about a thing," said Miller. "Just keep moving, keep moving," and he jiggled around in a little circle before the mechanic, holding his wine bottle in front of his chest like a rifle at port arms.

"You're so right, so right!" Schultz cried, but weakly, and he stood up and looked around the farmyard. It was rapidly getting dark. "What did you say about the bull? What about the bull?"

"He's beat," said Miller. "I think he's shot his wad. They got him over by the stable or whatever it is, giving him a pep talk, but it won't do any good."

Schultz looked and saw that the Italians had led the bull some distance from the cow and were standing around him, shouting and waving their arms, as though exhorting a prizefighter to come out of his corner just once more, to go out for just one more round.

"There's just so many shots in a clip," Miller said. "Or maybe this one never had any in him at all, they just thought he did."

"A reasonable assumption," Schultz said carefully. "As I seem to have said already, if you can't believe in a bull, what the hell can you believe in?"

Naturally, he thought, you can't believe in anything, I just went all through that, I thought, you can't hope for anything, and as long as you know that you're all right. It doesn't make any difference that there's no love, no faith, no truth, no tomorrow morning when everything's-going-to-be-all-right, and if you know that nothing can bother you. That's what I've been wanting to say to Moore, I've just been warming up to it, that's all, but wait a minute. Haven't I already told him? Looking at the crowd around the bull he tried to remember but couldn't, and then the crowd moved and he saw the bull clearly, his great, thick neck stretched out, low, his blocky, solid head turned, the horns showing clearly against the wall behind him even in the dying light. Schultz realized suddenly that it was nearly dark, that they had spent the afternoon drinking and waiting for something, he couldn't remember what, was it food? but anyway waiting a long time in the sun. And he also thought, without knowing why, something always happens when you least expect it, and he started for the bull.

He could hear Miller calling after him but he kept going, not looking back. I'm going to prove something, he said to himself, saying it angrily, exasperated, as though he had been arguing for hours with someone and had turned away at last to seize and present the absolute proof of his remarks. He came up to the Italians and the bull, which looked at him, and stood by the bull's head, not knowing why he had come there. The Italians seemed to welcome him, but with reserve, moving aside for him more out of politeness than eagerness to have him there. He realized, not caring, that they were disturbed by the bull's failure, that for them it was not something to joke about, perhaps especially not in front of the Americans, but he was bored and annoyed with these people.

"Give me that," he said to the man holding the rope, and took the cheap, worn line from the man's grudging hand and turned away, pulling on the rope, not looking to see whether the bull would follow or not. But he felt the slackness in the line and knew the bull was coming behind him as he walked back across the farmyard in the shadows toward the chair where Moore sat, where he had been sitting for hours, probably.

"Listen," Schultz called to Moore, while still thirty feet from him. "Listen, I want to tell you something, I just thought of it, the important thing is to survive, no matter what the bastards do to you. Like the bull! He's still alive, isn't he?"

"What are you doing?" Moore said, leaning forward and peering through the gloom. He sounded startled, like a man awakened in the night by a strange noise. "What's going on?"

"Never mind that," Schultz said impatiently, annoyed by the interruption. "This is important. You can't give in to the bloody system no matter what."

"You're drunker than you were before," Moore said. "Aren't we ever going back to the field? Let's get out of here, it's too dark to see now."

He stood up, ready to leave.

"All right, all right!" shouted Schultz, really angry now at these sticks Moore was shoving between his legs. "In a minute. But first, and this is important, I keep telling you, I've got something to say . . ."

"Is that the bull? Are you pulling that bull behind you?" Moore took a nervous step forward, then stopped. "You don't know what you're doing! Get him out of here!" and he retreated behind the ornate chair. "Are you crazy? Don't bring him over here!"

"Shut up!" Schultz shouted furiously. He raised his right arm and made an angry, throwing motion at Moore, throwing as hard as he could, but the movement halted in midflight, his arm was arrested strangely above his head as the rope he held in his right hand jerked up, taut, a hard line from his hand to the ring in the nose of the bull.

Of course, thought Schultz as he felt Miller's hands hard on his arm, pulling him, clawing at him, dragging him roughly until he fell awkwardly and heavily to the ground, he's had to put up with a lot today but I didn't hurt him that much, did I, and he felt the quick, searing pain as the rope ran out of his hand and the bull crashed past him like a carload of coal going down a steel chute. Lying on his back in the dirt he heard the bull's snort, the yelling, the screaming, and then, peculiarly, a crunching sound, like wooden plants splintering under pressure applied to the ends. It was a quick, very brief sound, almost lost in the other sounds, but Schultz thought he heard it very distinctly and as he lay there gasping for breath he realized what it was. The chair, he thought, the big bastard ran over the horsehair chair.

There was a sucking rush toward the open end of the farmyard, thudding and running and shouting, and then it was quiet. Schultz struggled to sit up, his lungs burning and pumping, then managed to stand, and over his breathing he heard a sound like someone sawing wood, far away, the sound of a crosscut saw rasping in deliberate rhythm through a plank, and then, in the farmyard, near him in the darkness, a wet, thick gargle. He looked and saw Miller on his knees, a faint smudge kneeling over Moore and the broken pieces of the horsehair chair.

That's impossible, he thought, a dull, numb feeling, and he walked, almost falling, stumbling on a bottle, until he fell to his knees beside Miller with the sawing and gargling louder and louder until it beat against his skull, surrounding him.

"No," he said, "no, is he hurt?" and he put his hand out, into a warm, quivering slime which he had not seen but which now gleamed faintly in the dark like wet pavement, Sergeant Moore's stomach and intestines.

"Ah," said Schultz, "Aah," and he tore with both hands at his scarf, jerking it from his neck and folding it into a thick, billowy square which he dropped into the slime. At once the white square began to disappear in the dark, it seemed to dissolve in patches as the liquid drowned it, until it was no longer visible, and Schultz was then aware that the sawing and gargling had stopped, that he and Miller were alone in the farmyard. They ran away, he thought, scared, or to catch the bull, and he got up and began walking toward the open end of the farmyard, where he remembered the gate was, not stopping as Miller called to him.

It's happened so often, he thought, so many thousands of times, it's everywhere, it's in the valley, it's up in the haze in the mountains, you find it wherever you go. There was one on the road to Mignano with the seat of his pants torn off, lying in the ditch where the dirt and trash collected around him for weeks, washing up against him like driftwood against a log, against a snag, collecting around his bare butt, and another one in the creek at Vairano, we finally pulled him out with a rope, and there was one in the field at Rocca, his face had been eaten away by the dogs and when we pulled off his tags the gas came out of him in a rush and a rumble, we threw up, there are thousands, they're everywhere, lying out there in the dark, but this is the first time I ever saw it happen, this is the first time it ever happened to me . . . Oh, God, hang on . . .

"We'll have to get the halftrack," he said without stopping or turning around. "We can't carry him like that," and he passed through the gate and turned toward the river. No, he thought, we certainly can't carry him like that, and he walked on in the darkness, waiting for it to rush at him, and trying to remember where they had crossed the dry riverbed.

my house in heilbronn

❧ In the beginning it must have looked like any other house, one you could find out on Gregory Boulevard in Kansas City or on Austin Avenue in Waco, Texas, perfectly ordinary, just ugly enough to be reassuring, so we took it. Besides, it was right across the railroad tracks from the field where we kept the Piper Cubs and the Fieseler Storch, so we ran the German family out and moved in with no more than the usual difficulty. I think they went to the aunt's house, I was never sure, somewhere near the station, or what had been the station, since nothing in that place was quite as it had been, everything was a little insane. Anyway, I never saw them again, or if I did I was unaware of it.

As I say, the house looked midwestern or even very late southern, but that mold had been at it for years so that it was a little blurred and softened, the way they all are over there, more so near the coast, of course, but you find it wherever you go. A smell of damp plaster, a clean cellar smell, and everything a little crumbly, the stucco flaking loose in your hand, like it had too much sand in it, not enough lime. In the gardens there are timid little terraces which don't amount to anything, connected by broken, crumbling little steps scaled for midgets, with pieces of

229

smashed bottles and cracked tiles stuck in the cement for decoration, and even concrete birdbaths shaped like huge champagne glasses, covered with shards of mirror and colored glass. And all this decaying somehow, even the blue gravel, like that you put in an aquarium or a rich man's driveway, silted with common rocks and tiny bits of broken pottery, slowly becoming adulterated.

And of course the beds were very different. In this house they were tremendous, and in my room there were two which could be pushed together, they were built that way, to form a really fantastic bed. In your sleep you could roam on it, or if you couldn't sleep you could thrash around in the worst possible temper and never fall out. The sheets always remained smooth, too, and although I don't remember ever changing them, they were never dirty. That's especially remarkable, since there was no bath in the house and at that time I didn't care about it too much. Every week or so I went across town to a house where a friend lived, and there I took a bath, a real one, American style, with lots of chromium, porcelain, hot water and thick towels. They had a wonderful place over there, I suppose there were at least twenty people living in the house but it was always quiet and orderly, or at least you got that impression, since the walls were thick and not cracked and the doors were well fitted, with metal weather stripping, even on the ones inside the house, leading from room to room or out in the halls. It was set well back from the street, too, you didn't get all the racket.

That was one of the troubles with our place, of course. It was too small, the people hadn't had enough money, I suppose, and the street ran right by our front door, and then on the other side of the street was the railroad, on an embankment ten feet high, so that the engines blew steam and cinders all over the joint. It was a hell of a place, really, but by the time we found that out it was too late to do anything about it, or we were too lazy. It was summer then, too, and hotter than you'd have expected, certainly too hot to think of moving.

To our right, as you came out the front door, was a big orchard of some sort, about a hundred yards square, and then a house and more houses. I'd never been down there before the old man came that afternoon, it was on the way out of town, not in, and I never went out of town. Even the orchard didn't interest us, I remember, we thought there was nothing in it, to eat, I mean, until that same afternoon, and by then it was all over, of course, the way it always was. You got so damned sick of that!

No, we were just conscious of our house, the road, the God-damned railroad, and on the other side of that, the equally damned airplanes, which by this time we hated thoroughly, as you can imagine. It finally got so we never went near them at all, just left them tied up for weeks at a time, with the sun swelling the gasoline until it ran out over the cowlings. If anybody came down and was insistent about going for a ride or taking a message somewhere we were ready with involved stories to put them off, technical details about engine breakdowns, and so on. At one point we even went so far as to disassemble the brake connections on the Storch, and then we would take people over there and show them the disconnected tubing, if they insisted. They couldn't understand it all, of course, so finally they'd go away. Everybody was alike that summer, everything was too much bother, it was easier to forget it, whatever it was.

So when the old man came running up that afternoon I was ready to kill him, I really was, but even that was too much trouble. I couldn't help thinking of all the explaining that would have to be done, all the questions and answers and forms, the replies by endorsement, you know how it is, and as a matter of fact I didn't even have anything handy to kill him with, if it came to that. My pistol was buried in a barracks bag someplace, so I couldn't even scare him off.

In fact I didn't look very military at all, I think he was disappointed. I was sitting out in that idiotic garden on a folding canvas chair I'd had made in Italy, in Positano, out of a shelter-half, wearing the most worn and faded coveralls I had because they were the most comfortable, with a pair of canvas shoes with rope soles on my feet. No socks. The shoes came from Positano, too, I'd bought them right after I traded a limey out of a pair of khaki shorts, because at that time I was determined to live a comfortable war and I did, I even taught our Italian PW, Guido, his name was, from Tivoli, we picked him up near Venafro, to make tea every afternoon about four. He'd have it hot for me when I got down from the afternoon mission, people couldn't get over it. Two Britishers flopped down on our strip near Vairano Patenora one afternoon in one of those heavy, tailskid jobs they used for spotting, blind as a bat behind, and they were amazed by it all, me in my rope-soled shoes and shorts, Guido brewing up, it was a hell of a thing. I enjoyed it, they thought they were in the wrong army, or I was. Well, the hell with them.

Anyway, I heard the old fellow coming through the orchard like a wounded buffalo, yelling his head off in that stupid language of theirs, and I was mad at him before he ever crashed into the garden, because as a matter of fact I'd never heard one of them shout before, they weren't doing any hollering just then, you know, although of course I suppose in the good old days they did nothing else, if you remember the newsreels.

Well, here he came, really letting loose, right up in front of me in my chair, with my glass of vermouth and another case where that came from. That was one thing, that town had two big industries in it: a pickle factory and a vermouth distillery, a wonderful combination. I lived on the stuff. The British had really clobbered the place about a year before, on a lovely spring evening, we heard, with everybody out for a stroll, thinking the ships were on the way to Stuttgart, but they hadn't ruined the pickle factory or the vermouth works. They got the dehydrated soup plant and the powdered milk company, that was all finished by the time we got there, thank God, but they just shook up the pickles and the vermouth. There was plenty left for everybody, all you had to do was go and pick it up, and we certainly did. In fact everybody was half drunk all the time and stuffed with pickles. I'd like to tell you about the Fourth of July celebration they tried to arrange, when everybody in the battalion showed up stewed, including the colonel, and they damned near blew the pickle works down trying to fire all eighteen M-7's in a salute, but that doesn't have anything to do with this.

So anyway, when the old bastard got up close to me I took a kick at him, without getting out of my chair or sloshing my drink around, so of course I missed. He quit yelling for a split second, then he went right on, really rolling it out, and me not under-standing a word. You know how it is, you can get it one word at a time, if they try real hard to make it sound like English, but when they really cut loose it's impossible. So there we were, me in the chair not saying anything for a minute, and him hopping around in front of me like he was going out of his mind.

He was a real old bird, in his seventies, I suppose, a tough-looking grandpa type, sort of, and he had a red and blue lump on his head which really was as big as a chicken's egg. I mean, you hear that all the time, but this really was, sticking up on his bald head like that it was enough to turn your stomach.

"Where'd you get that?" I said, and I pointed at his head, and that speeded him up a little, he was donder-and-blitzening like a five-alarm fire after that, pointing at his head and then back at the orchard, jumping up and down on the gravel until, like I say, I really could have killed him just to have a little peace and quiet.

I really didn't give a damn, but the first thing I thought was that he'd caught some soldiers in his orchard and tried to run them off and they'd slugged him, so now he was after me to do some-thing about it. If that was it that was just too bad, of course, in those days you could do just about anything you damn well pleased and nobody cared about it, you know, although I hear it's different now, and so much the worse for our side, and certainly I wasn't about to get up and start running around just because some jerks had tried to steal his apples, or whatever they were. Anyway, I didn't think there were any apples or anything else in the orchard, you never found a damn thing growing that you could eat, they always picked it and hid it, you know, so I was pretty cool to the whole idea. I just sat there, and every once in a while I'd take a kick at him when he got too close, slopping up that vermouth, and occasionally I'd holler, *"Raus!"* just to show him how I felt about it all. I was mad at him, all right, but it was too hot to start anything and I figured I could sweat him out, just sitting in my chair in the shade, with the vermouth bottle almost full, and I think I would have, if the girl hadn't come up the steps from the road.

She wasn't anything special, just another fraulein like all the others, sort of drab and fat-looking, with clothes that you couldn't remember as soon as you looked away from her, but the old man acted like she was Lili Marlene in the flesh. He turned the hose on her, waving at the orchard and pointing at that knot on his head, while I just sat there and watched them. The girl had one of those leatherette satchels over her arm like they all carry over there, and I suppose she'd been scrounging around uptown someplace, without too much luck, because the satchel wasn't full. She looked pretty crumby all around, in fact. And then she started speaking English to me.

"My grandfather says you must help us," she said, looking straight at me, the old I'm-not-afraid-of-you con, you know, I've got a brother in the Wehrmacht who could lick you anytime, if he ever gets home, where've you got him cooped up, anyway. One of those. Bubba ain't coming home, he's fertilizing a rock up in the Liri valley someplace, but that doesn't make any difference, they're just as bitter, just as smart-alecky, until you bear down on them, of course. Then it's me no Alamo, me no Goliad all over the place, they never heard of Hitler. Isn't Hindenburg still president? you know, that kind of stuff. I used to tell them I was a Jew, just to throw the needle into them, and it always worked.

Well, I was all set to tell her to take the old man and buzz off, I wasn't in any mood to start breaking her down, making her admit she'd been in the Hitler Youth and had a cousin in the SS, and so on, the way you could if you didn't have anything else to do, so I just gave her the quickie.

"I'm a Jew," I said. "*Jude.*"

Like I say, it never failed, because my nose was broken when I was a kid, it's flattened out enough to make it sound plausible, and when you add that to what they all carry around in their minds it's more than enough. Or it always was, anyway. The girl blushed, and she looked at the old man, who quit jabbering as soon as he heard that "*Jude,*" and then she looked back at me.

"I'm sorry," she said.

"Well, I'll be a son of a bitch!" I hollered, and this time I got up. "Sorry!"

Well, I was really going to lay into them good, muscle them out in the street with a few well-placed boots in their sitdowns and maybe pop somebody one, but she started talking again about helping her grandfather, fast, almost too fast for her English, and talking about the train, and it really was so damned hot and as I said before nobody had much energy that summer, you couldn't get too worked up about anything, so I let it go.

"What train?" I said. "What are you talking about?" and she said the train on our tracks, right across the street, only it hadn't come up to our house yet. It was sitting out there, waiting for a clearance into the yards, I suppose, so I hadn't seen it, and even if it had been right in front of me I might not have noticed it, I was so sick and tired of the damned things.

That was what I had to help them about, she said, the trouble came from the train, that was why the old man had the egg on his head. That sounded to me like the silliest thing I'd ever heard of, I couldn't figure out how the old man could have fiddled around and been hit by the train, especially since it wasn't even moving, but you never know what you're going to run across over there.

Once in France I saw a guy carrying a bicycle along on the highway shoulder, he turned to look behind him, swinging the bike's front wheel out in the road when he did it, and a halftrack hit the wheel and left him spinning like a top. You know how it is, there's always something screwy like that going on, with that many people running all over the country it can't be helped.

Anyway, I thought about the train a while, and about sitting in that broken-down garden, and I had to admit it, it was pretty boring. That's the way it would be in those days, you'd get so bored you'd want to do something, but you couldn't, the boredom was so heavy you really couldn't move unless somebody came along and stirred you up, it was like being in a barrel full of warm wax. So I thought, what the hell, let's go look at the train, either these two will get themselves into more trouble while we're looking at it or something will happen, anyway, it'll make a story to tell at mess, so we went down the steps, across the street and up on the embankment.

The locomotive was there, about a hundred yards down the track, with a long string of boxcars behind it. As soon as I saw the damn thing I knew what it was, there were people all over the cars, up on the roofs, whole families of them, there were even some birds on the cowcatcher. It was a DP train, I suppose there were two thousand people and a million lice riding on it, all happy as could be, going from nowhere to nowhere, just riding around the country like the trainmen's union on a picnic, without a worry in the world.

We walked along on the ballast beside the tracks, and all the people looked down at us, grinning at me and laughing at the bump on the old man's head. They thought that was killing, they hollered back into the cars for everybody to come and have a look and everybody did, women, children and old folks all looking out at us like we were there for their own amusement and were really measuring up to what they had expected. The happiest bunch you've ever seen! They always were, those people, they thought they were going home, wherever that is.

And while we walked along, the ballast hurting my feet through the rope soles, the girl told me the whole damned train-load had jumped off when the cars had stopped and had boiled down into her granddaddy's orchard like the opening of the Cherokee strip in Cimarron. I guess they really went through the place like an armored division on the run, because when I saw it later the limbs were broken off of all the trees and some of the smaller trees were knocked clear over, like a big wind had hit them. They were after the fruit, of course, but I never found out what it was. If the girl told me I didn't hear her and I'm afraid I can't tell one tree from another. Anyway, Grandpa heard the racket and came busting out, of course, and that's when the lights went out. And now, the girl said, they wanted me to find the guilty parties, that's exactly what she said, and punish them.

I ask you! I couldn't believe my ears for a minute, I looked at her and at the old man, then up and down that trainload of happy, smiling savages, because that's what they really were like, they had nothing to lose, you know, they could've taken over the whole town in ten minutes if it had ever entered their heads, and I really couldn't believe it, but that's what the old man had in mind. Law and order! Payment for damages! Arrest the criminals! I like to fell over, right there, it was the biggest idea I'd heard of in a long, long time, and certainly the most impossible. It was on a par with the remarks I heard a corps commander make to the officers of the 36th Division, just before we went into southern France. "I don't want to hear of anybody being pinned down by machine guns or mortars," he screeched in that high little voice, standing up there in his riding pants and boots, no bigger than my wife. "Don't send back any messages about being pinned down on the beach by machine guns!" The idiot! It didn't have anything to do with me, we took off from LST's with plywood decks after they had the beach, but the nerve of the jerk, I couldn't get over it.

And now the old man, wanting me to go through a trainload of DP's from every country east of the Rhine, asking who busted down his fruit trees and slugged him, with the train probably ready to pull out in five minutes, come hell or high water, even if I was Eisenhower. And the son of a bitch was a kraut! After all they'd been busy at for fifteen years, now he wanted everything straightened out about his orchard, that's why he got me out of my chair and away from my vermouth. And then I remembered I'd forgotten to cork the bottle and it would probably be full of gnats when I got back, that whole town was lousy with gnats, I suppose because of the distillery, and then I did start to get mad.

I grabbed the old man and the girl and marched them across the street into the orchard, and believe me, it was a mess, like I said. I pulled them along between the beat-up trees and I was just getting ready to stop at a good distance from the train and start making a big speech to the old geezer, with the girl translating, when I felt my foot slip in something and I looked down and there it was: a big pile of you-know-what, a little souvenir left by one of the DP's, they don't have toilets on those box cars but even if they did I imagine he'd have left it anyway, a little fertilizer for the old bastard to get a fresh start with on his new orchard. And me wearing canvas shoes with rope soles!

Well, that did it. I jerked the old man around and started hollering at him, showing him my shoe, and then I saw that wasn't going to do any good so I hauled off and popped him one, right in the guts, and when he bent over I shoved him so he fell down, and then I cleaned my shoe as best I could on the seat of his pants. I'd have dragged his face into that mess if it hadn't been so much trouble and so damned hot, but as it was I just gave him a good boot in the face with the sole of my shoe and went home, being careful where I walked.

And sure enough, the bottle neck was full of gnats, I had to throw the damn thing away, and right after I did that the train came by and blew cinders and dirt all over me before I could get inside with the windows shut. That was really a hell of a place, that house was, except for the beds in my room.

the death of
william faulkner

:: He had been in pain for several weeks, wearing a brace to support the injured back, and people around the square said maybe that was why he started drinking again. The bourbon came down from Memphis, although the nearest bootlegger was seventeen miles from town and Memphis was more like seventy. But the bootlegger has a very limited stock and, besides, if you buy from him, everybody knows how much you're drinking. They know you're drinking anyway, but they don't know how much, and that came to be a matter of some satisfaction—or of pride—in Oxford, Mississippi.

He had been trying to quit drinking altogether, and he had; but two weeks before, he'd gone out on a new horse, and the horse came back without him. The cook saw the horse come back and told his wife, and she found him in the red-clay cut where the new highway was going in just south of town. He said the horse had "roached its back" and thrown him, and it hurt, and he told a friend of his, "A horse ain't got much sense. A mule has more sense. A mule will take care of you as well as himself."

But anyway, that started the drinking again, said the people around the square, because his back hurt him, and he'd taken a couple of bad falls from a horse not long before that up in Virginia. He got medicine for the pain at the drugstore on the square, but it wasn't enough, so the bourbon started coming down again from Memphis. That's what they said.

"He used to come in every day to get that medicine," the druggist says. "Walk all the way in from the house. It was that damn horse. Which horse was it?" says the druggist, who is not a horse-loving man but a courthouse-square man, in a starched white shirt and a bow tie. "Was it that mare—that big, old one?"

"No," says a man at the counter, drinking Coca-Cola and eating Nab crackers of peanut butter and cheese. "That's Temptress, the mare. This was a new horse, way I hear tell it. Temptress wouldn't never of throwed him. His niggers call her Tempie."

The man who knows about Tempie wears khaki trousers and a blue work shirt, and the back of his neck is red and cracked. He knows the family, but at a distance, the way most of the town knows the family. He does not know the writer, the famous man. He knows Mr. Bill, the member of the family, but knows him as he knows the other members of the family—at a distance, because this family, and a few others, are aloof from the town. They move through it and above it, doing things which are often incomprehensible to the town but which are never really questioned, because there are some families you just don't question: You nod and say hello if you are spoken to, or, if not, you get out of the way.

"His great-granddaddy, now," says the druggist. "He built a railroad all the way down from Memphis, and it never made a dime. Lost his shirt. But that's how they are. Don't seem to give a damn one day, just as nice as they can be the next. You never know where you stand. But fine folks. Just not too sociable."

No, not sociable with the town, maybe not even with each other: withdrawn, and brooding, and then smiling, nodding, tipping the hat or the old tweed cap, strolling uptown in khakis and an old Burberry trench coat with the bloodstains of long-dead deer on it. On those days you could say hello and even stop to visit awhile on the street about the weather or the crops or horses or the government, but on other days you stepped aside and you didn't say hello. And sometimes the presence would vanish from the streets and the town for days or weeks or months and everybody said, "Ah, yes, it's started up again," and some of them smirked in private. The town's famous son, who was never the favorite son, who would not have the honor were it offered because—some said—he was too modest. Modesty, perhaps, or perhaps an aristocratic contempt, but anyway, no favorite.

"There's not a lot of our people read too much," says the town librarian. She sits in the library, a small room upstairs in the courthouse, in front of a glass-doored bookcase with the famous man's books locked inside. "He didn't come up here often," she says apologetically. "He had quite a few books himself, and of course he could use the university when he needed it. We're all very upset. It was that horse, wasn't it? That Tempie, that old mare of his?"

"I was out fishing with him, just a couple of weeks ago," says Aubrey Seay. Mr. Seay has white hair and a scarlet face, and he owns The Mansion restaurant in Oxford. The Mansion is a sort of compressed version of an antebellum mansion, with white columns out front, but they are just short columns, not much more than one-story high.

"His back was hurting him then," says Mr. Seay, sitting in one of the back booths of The Mansion. "We went out to the lake and used my boat. He was crazy about boats, you know. Not many people outside of around here know that. Sailboats, especially. But that day we just went fishing and had a couple of drinks. A few drinks, I guess you might say. Nothing out of the way. We just talked when he wanted to talk, mostly about fishing and about politics some.

"He said that if there was any trouble when it came time for that Meredith fellow to enter the university it would be folks from

Beat Two that caused it. Beat Two? Beat Two is the rough part of town, kind of like what you call up north a precinct. Instead of precinct, we say beat, just like we say high sheriff instead of just sheriff. I don't know exactly where the word comes from. Probably it comes from the old days, when a night watchman walked a beat, wouldn't you say? Mr. Faulkner would've been able to tell you about that in a minute.

"It was amazing how much knowledge that man had. It used to tickle me when I'd read in some magazine or book about how he had never really had much education. Shoot, he was one of the most educated men you ever saw, and one of the most gentlemanly. He and Miss Estelle, that's Mrs. Faulkner, you know, they used to come in two or three times a week for supper. He always had a filet mignon, and they sat in the same booth every time.

"Before we got the Muzak we had a jukebox and I always had to disconnect it when he came in. He didn't like it. And once, I remember, oh, it was years ago, he and Miss Estelle came in and I disconnected the jukebox and some college boys went over and connected it up again and started playing it, and he and Miss Estelle got up and left without a word, and do you know, they didn't come back for about a year, maybe longer. I felt terrible about it, but I couldn't go up to him on the street and say it was just an accident. In some way or other he blamed me for it, and he'd just nod to me, real short, on the street, for all of that time. Then one night they came back in for supper, just as pleasant as could be, as though nothing had happened. After we got the Muzak I always turned it off as soon as he'd come in."

In the back of The Mansion is a large, high-ceilinged, rather empty-looking room where service clubs hold their luncheons. High along one wall runs a balustraded balcony, and Mr. Seay likes to recall that the only time the Faulkner family ever gave a party in living memory, they gave it in that room.

"It was for his daughter and some of her friends," Mr. Seay says, looking up at the balcony. "The children danced down here and the Faulkners sat up on the balcony, watching. It was strange, like something out of the old times, I suppose. I hate to say it, but it wasn't a very lively party. I think the young folks were kind of held back, having the family up there looking on that way."

The formidable family. St. Peter's Cemetery is full of them, lying under curious, Victorian monuments; a cenotaph bears two white marble portraits of a man and woman: under one is the word, MOTHER, under the other, FATHER. Near them a small stone set in the grass:

DEAN SWIFT FAULKNER
1907–1935
I BORE HIM ON EAGLE'S WINGS
AND BORE HIM UNTO ME.

Dean Swift Faulkner: brother of William, killed in the crash of a Waco biplane near Water Valley, south of town. William had given him the Waco, and there was mystery in its crash, something no one wants to talk about, even now.

If you stay in Oxford long enough, you see that the incidents in Faulkner's novels are, to an astonishing degree, taken from the life of his family and his town. In *Sartoris,* the novel about the aristocratically doomed family which appears to approach his own most closely, and the one about which he wrote most romantically, the death of Dean Swift Faulkner appears in altered form: There was a Sartoris in 1918 who flew his Sopwith Camel up where the Fokker D VII's waited, knowing they would kill him; there was another Sartoris who deliberately flew an experimental aircraft past its point of endurance, and died at Wright Field. The aristocratic Sartorises, willfully bent on defying Heaven itself, or fleeing Heaven itself, or determined to outdo other mortals even if to die. The Sartorises never say why; they never explain. Neither do the Faulkners. The talkiness and blabber of self-explanation are too modern, not Faulknerian at all: except for airplanes, William was not a very modern sort of man, everybody says, and perhaps to him the airplanes of his youth were just chargers of the air, beasts to bear young knights to battle.

He did not even like telephones. He was slightly deaf in one ear, and when you called the house it was always Miss Estelle you talked with.

"I remember when we were making arrangements about the portrait," says Dr. James Webb, chairman of the university's English department. The idea of the portrait came about because a seventy-year-old painter named Murray Lloyd Goldsborough was in town for an eye operation. "I made this appointment with Miss Estelle for them to come over and talk about it, and just about the time they were due she called up and said they would be a little late, because he was out in the paddock then, spreading manure.

"Mr. Goldsborough had almost lost his sight," says Dr. Webb around his professorial pipe. "He had done portraits of some of the university officials in the past, and once he painted Kaiser Wilhelm's portrait, but he was losing his sight and he'd come here for an operation by Dr. Joseph Rogers. When he felt better, he said he'd like to do a portrait of Faulkner. I approached Mr. Faulkner, and he said he didn't mind one way or the other but if we wanted it done he'd sit for it. He and Miss Estelle drove over that day in their red Rambler station wagon, and I remember Mr. Faulkner had a bourbon and Miss Estelle had coffee. I had a cognac. I remember Faulkner lit his pipe very ceremoniously, not just like any man lighting his pipe. There was something impressive about it. Then he discovered his chair was on a floor register and he moved it, in case the heat came on.

"Mr. Goldsborough and Mr. Faulkner talked about mutual friends for a while, and then Mr. Goldsborough said he thought it would be a good idea if Mr. Faulkner posed for the portrait in an academic gown. The university had discussed giving Mr. Faulkner an honorary degree but never had, and Mr. Faulkner said he'd refused several honorary Ph.D.'s because he'd never earned one, as others had. He was wearing an English tweed jacket and a pair of dirty khakis that day, so I suggested he pose in that, sitting in some favorite chair. Faulkner said, yes, he had a favorite chair, one he could 'just squash down in' and be comfortable. So that's what he sat in. It's a pink chair, really, but in the portrait, it's green. Miss Estelle said she was pleased the university was having the portrait done, and I remember she talked about how she protected him from visitors so he would have time for writing and riding. For some reason he never wrote in the summertime, you know.

"Then I recall we started talking about horses and somebody said you should use French to women, Italian to men and German to horses. Mr. Faulkner said he used Anglo-Saxon and he thought the horses understood him. Even his small talk was sententious. We began talking about French participles, which he knew very well, and from that we got onto the subject of animals, and Mr. Faulkner said the rat was the smartest of all animals. Then Mrs. Goldsborough started talking about how difficult it is to save money, and she said she even cut her husband's hair. Mrs. Faulkner asked Mr. Faulkner if he'd let her do that, and he said he'd pay what it was worth."

Dr. Webb sits in his study, in the basement of his house out near the university, and recalls in fine detail his encounters with the great man, the great writer. He has kept copious notes, including a description of Faulkner's living room. These show that it contained, among other things, a wood carving of a human head, some Japanese vases on the mantel, and on top of a bookcase, a stuffed horned owl sitting on a sweet-gum branch. When Callie Barr died about 1940, her funeral was held in that living room, and Faulkner conducted the service himself. Callie was the Negro mammy who raised William, and for years she had a favorite rocker in the living room which was inviolate. Earl Wortham, the Negro blacksmith who shod the Faulkner horses, remembers seeing William with Callie fifty or sixty years ago, walking down the street.

"She'd say, 'Now, you get up here on the sidewalk, Billy,' and he'd say, 'I ain't gonna do it.' He liked walking in the dust of the road."

A reporter from the Memphis *Press-Scimitar* named Edwin Howard asked Earl if he knew Mr. Faulkner's last book was about the livery stable where Earl worked as a child and about a horse race, and Earl said, yes, Mr. Bill had told him he was writing about a race up in Tennessee. Since that last book, *The Reivers*, is also about a wild trip to Memphis in a Model T, the reporter asked Earl if he remembered ever making such a trip, and Earl said, no, he never had done so.

"But Chester Carruthers did," Earl said. "He was the Colonel's driver. The Colonel was Mr. Bill's granddaddy. The Colonel's car was made right here in town out of an old buggy. A man named John Buffalo, used to live right up there on the hill, built it."

Oxford is Jefferson, and Lafayette County is Yoknapatawpha County, there is no mistaking it, standing in the July heat of the courthouse square, the galleried buildings around the four sides, the lawyers' offices above the drugstores and drygoods stores and hardware stores, the courthouse as white as fresh plaster, the Confederate soldier on his column a little streaked and graying now, and, under the trees of the courthouse lawn, the Negroes selling melons and tomatoes and ears of sweet corn: it is astonishing how much Oxford is Jefferson. Wrought-iron railings run around the galleries up above, and you climb tilted, splintered wooden stairs to peer through dirty glass into deserted offices. One windowed door has JOHN FAULKNER, ATTORNEY, painted dimly on it in fading, peeling paint, and beyond the cobwebbed glass is an empty room, thick with dust and heat.

Everything from the novels is in Oxford, either present or remembered: There are families with names Faulkner might have used, such as the Fudge family. There is Basil Fudge, Buren Fudge, Earl Fudge, Euphus Fudge, Glynn Fudge, Jack Fudge and James Culley Fudge. Where is Frenchman's Bend? Mr. Seay smiles and says he thinks he knows. And the store from *Intruder in the Dust?* "Why," says a man in the drugstore, "that's out at College Hill, ain't it? Always heard it was. No, I never read the book." And perhaps for those who live in Oxford reading the books would seem merely repetition, the events part of the town's shared experience and recollection, experience and recollection immediately familiar to the Southerner no matter where he may be; always strange, Gothic, bizarre and melodramatic to those outside the South. And even now, in this death, there was something strange, and the reporters knew it.

The first wire-service stories said William Faulkner had died in Oxford, and we came to Oxford believing it. But soon, in guarded conversations, in looks, in smiles, we were not quite told the truth but pointed toward it. No one could say which hospital Mr. Faulkner died in; no one could say he died at home, the big white house behind the trees on the south end of town. Could one ask at the house? No, there was a policeman stationed at the lane leading to it, standing there beneath the old cedars, sweating in the heat and keeping everybody out.

Finally someone discovered the body had been brought to Oxford early on the morning of Friday, July sixth, in a hearse belonging to the Douglass Funeral Home. Before the funeral director could order him not to talk, the driver said, yes, he had gone to Byhalia early Friday morning for the body. Where in Byhalia? At an alcoholic clinic there, the driver said. Byhalia is on the road to Memphis, north of Holly Springs, and in Oxford everybody knows about the clinic. And it seemed everyone knew that Faulkner had died there, some said in a convulsion, some said in a fall downstairs. Mrs. Faulkner was with him when he died, everyone said. As for proof, there was none. The superintendent of the clinic wouldn't talk, and the death certificate gave Oxford as the place of death. The family wanted it that way, everyone said.

In a room at the Ole Miss Motel the reporters gathered and talked about it, and—already impressed, perhaps, by the implacability of that formidable family—agreed to forget Byhalia. You couldn't prove it, and besides, what difference did it make? We were there because a great man was dead, not because a man had died in an alcoholic clinic.

The family. Two of William's brothers asked to see the reporters the night before the funeral and we met in that dimly lighted empty room at the back of Mr. Seay's Mansion restaurant, at a table with ice and bottles and glasses and the remains of the reporters' steak dinners. J. M. Faulkner came, a Marine colonel, a spare, taut-skinned man with a Marine haircut, and with him his older brother Murry, heavier, looking tired, not as frightening as the colonel. Murry is an FBI agent in Mobile, Alabama, and the family spokesman. Mr. Seay introduced everyone, and the Faulkner brothers murmured politely and shook hands.

We all sat down, and Murry said the family wanted to make certain there would be no unpleasant scene, no disturbance at the funeral. For him to meet us at all was obviously distasteful: he did not approve our presence or our occupations, and he politely declined a drink. Nobody mentioned Byhalia. Someone asked if the casket would be open, and both brothers spoke together: Absolutely not. Paul Flowers, a vast, jovial, red-faced and sweating man who writes a column for the Memphis *Commercial Appeal,* told the brothers they could count on our decorum.

What about the services? They would be private, at the home with only family and close friends, no reporters. Another brief service would be held at the grave.

"Ordinarily, in a matter of this kind, we would not tolerate the publicity and notoriety which will attend my brother's funeral," Murry Faulkner said. "However, we are well aware of his fame and of his accomplishments, and we understand that you gentlemen are here from a sense of duty to your employers, rather than morbid curiosity. We wish to help you all we can. But decorum and dignity must be preserved. I know you all appreciate that."

We assured him that we did appreciate that, and, after once more declining a drink, the brothers left the restaurant.

The burial was to take place Saturday afternoon. Saturday morning two Negroes were digging the grave, in the "new" section of St. Peter's Cemetery. The old section is a rolling turf, with mossy, dignified headstones and Victorian cenotaphs and a grove of ancient cedars near the Faulkner burying ground where Dean Swift Faulkner lies. There are crepe myrtle, boxwood and magnolias there, but that burying ground is full: they were burying William in the new section, a raw slash of bulldozed clay and sandy soil below the hill, treeless except for a small clump of oaks.

Below the oaks Elbert and Will Houston dug by turns with long-handled shovels. It was not yet ten o'clock in the morning, but the temperature was already in the nineties, and their shirts and overall straps were dark with sweat. Richard Elliott, the mayor of Oxford who is also the director of the Douglass Funeral Home, stood under the awning over the grave site and watched, wearing a straw snap-brim hat, spotless starched white shirt, polka-dot tie and dark trousers. On the ground lay the raw lumber box which had held the casket and which would be used to shore up the sides of the grave, once the Houstons had dug it. A tag was tacked on the box: TEXARKANA CASKET CO., TEXARKANA, TEXAS. FUNERAL SUPPLIES. DO NOT DELAY. Well, they were not delaying. Some people around the square said it seemed a little peculiar, burying a famous man in such haste. There wouldn't be time for people to come from all over the world, they said around the square, people you know would want to be at the funeral. Besides, this haste was not in the southern tradition, and there was to be no viewing of the deceased in the casket. Peculiar, said the people around the square, but Mr. Elliott said the family wanted it that way.

"You know," he said, his face a little troubled. "You know how they are. They're a proud family, have reason to be. An old family. They don't necessarily do things the way other families do. They don't have to. And we all respect them for it here in Oxford. The headstone? Well, they haven't said anything about one yet. Well, yes, that might be a little peculiar for some families, not picking out a stone, but the Faulkner family . . ."

("If Bill had his way," says a man on the square, "they'd carry him out to the burial yard in a wagon behind a mule and drop him into the ground. He didn't give a damn for all this folderol of funerals, and caskets and taking on. He wasn't much for church either.")

"No," says the Reverend Duncan Gray, Jr., of St. Peter's Episcopal Church, "Mr. Faulkner did not attend services regularly. Mrs. Faulkner more frequently, perhaps."

"One time he said," says Aubrey Seay, " 'If I were reincarnated, I'd want to come back as a buzzard. Nothing hates him, or envies him, or wants him, or needs him; he's never bothered or in danger, and he can eat anything.' He loved a good joke and a good story, and he could tell one too. One of his favorites the last time I saw him was about the farmer who was down plowing in the field when his little chap came running up to him. 'Daddy,' says the little chap, 'They's a preacher up to the house and Mama says for you to come up right away.' Well, the farmer studies awhile, and then he says to the boy, 'You run on back up to the house, and if it's a Episcopal preacher, you tell your Ma to give him a cup of coffee. If it's a Methodist preacher, tell her to start frying up a chicken. But if it's a Baptist preacher, you set in your Ma's lap till I gets to the house.' Oh, he did love a good story. We're all sure going to miss him."

Elbert Houston hands his shovel over to Will and climbs out of the grave for a drink of water. He says it's harder digging than it looks, because of the roots of the oaks.

"But they'll shade the grave all the while except maybe just at noon," says Elbert. "He was a mighty nice man—to me, at least. I used to handle his horses some, and then I took care of his daughter's ponies, Miss Jill's ponies. He was always a good man."

"Elbert, we got to get it done before the flowers come," says Mr. Elliott.

"Yes, sir," says Elbert, and goes back into the grave.

"The flowers are coming in from everywhere," says Mr. Elliott. "I don't know where we'll put them all."

The body is lying in the back room of the Douglass Funeral Home and no one can see it. No one in Oxford will see it, except for the man who drove the hearse and Mr. Elliott.

"The casket," Mr. Elliot says, "is gray steel. It will be closed, because the family wish it closed. They asked me to tell you that for these last few hours he belongs to them; after the service, he belongs to the world."

He belongs to the world. An accurate statement, perhaps, but pompous, nonetheless. The reporters are a little annoyed, not at Faulkner, but at the family. You think of Addie Bundren's death and the journey of her corpse in *As I Lay Dying*: no pomposity of "belonging to the world" there, but only the pathetic, desperately comic trial of the Bundren family, trying to move that rotting flesh across the earth to a burying place, the husband false to her life and incomprehensible to her sons, and all of them toiling across the countryside, burdened with the corpse, an embarrassment but a duty. In a wagon, behind a mule. And now there is gray steel from Texarkana and more flowers than anyone knows what to do with, and the morning paper says Bennett Cerf is in Memphis, talking to reporters at the Peabody Hotel about how great was William Faulkner and how Bennett Cerf had always wanted to visit Oxford but never had. "Bill kept asking me to come down," says Bennett Cerf in the *Commercial Appeal*, "but I never got around to it. I'm sorry now I didn't."

But he will be in Oxford for the funeral, and so will William Styron and Shelby Foote and Donald Klopfer and many others. President Kennedy has sent a telegram expressing his regret at the death of one of the "great creators of his age," a man who "sought to illuminate the restless searching of all men," and nobody is going to get up in public now and tell about the time he said that he'd like to be reincarnated as a buzzard.

At the house, there is a private ceremony: Styron attends, as the guest of Bennett Cerf, and writes about it later. At the cemetery the other reporters wait on a little knoll above the tented grave and the folding metal chairs. The black Cadillac hearse comes down the drive from the house on the other side of town, moving slowly over the naked roots of the giant cedars, turns left and then left again, coming up the street toward the courthouse in the square. There are not many people on the streets. Everything is quiet. The hearse goes around the courthouse, past the Confederate soldier on his column, and on to the cemetery.

The cameras grind and whir in the silence as the gray metal casket is lifted from the hearse and the family and friends follow it. Mrs. Faulkner—Miss Estelle—is in a beige-and-black dress, with a broad-brimmed black straw hat which hides her face. She is supported by two male relatives to her seat beneath the canvas fly and sinks into a chair, her head lowered. The daughter Jill is bareheaded, blonde, solemn. Nobody speaks. The heat is violent, beyond belief. Sweat is dripping from the reporters' noses as they stand in the sun, splotching their notes; sweat shines on the high forehead of the Reverend Duncan Gray as he reads from *The Book of Common Prayer,* and then it is over. The family drives away; outsiders stand in the heat and tell each other of their departure plans. The town has not attended the funeral, just as the town did not much attend the life. Almost without notice the casket is lowered, the dirt is shoveled in, and the mound is heaped with gaudy, crisp and brilliant flowers until the grave itself is hidden, and everyone departs.

The reporters are ashen with heat and hangover, suddenly agitated by their deadlines. Styron is off for Martha's Vineyard; Claude Sitton of the *Times* says we'll all be back in September, when Meredith will try his luck at the university, and we scatter; so much we have not told, so much we have not learned, can never learn now, about that complicated family and its greatest, most complicated son. When we return in September, there is still no marker on his grave, so that those who were not present for his burial might not indeed know where he lies. Since then a large and handsome monument has been placed there, but it is for the living—the family and the world—not for the dead. Oxford's famous son, say the people on the square, would have liked it better the other way.